GENERAL MATHEMATICAL ABILITY

COMPLETE TEST PREPARATION, EXAMINATION, AND REVIEW FOR THE
MATHEMATICS PART OF THE HIGH SCHOOL EQUIVALENCY EXAMINATION (GED)

by EUGENE GUERCIO, B.S., CARMINE C. CASTELLANO, B.Ae., M.B.A.,
and CLIFFORD P. SEITZ, B.A., M.A., Ph.D.

ARCO PUBLISHING COMPANY, Inc.

NEW YORK

Published by Arco Publishing Company, Inc.
219 Park Avenue South, New York, N.Y. 10003

Library of Congress Catalog Card Number 74-19738
ISBN 0-668-03841-1 (Library Edition)
ISBN 0-668-03689-3 (Paper Edition)

Printed in the United States of America

CONTENTS

INTRODUCTION

SECTION I: Whole Numbers—Arithmetic Operations

SECTION II: Combination of Whole Number Operations

SECTION III: Fractions

SECTION IV: Decimals and Decimals to Fractions

SECTION X: Using Algebra to Solve Formula Problems

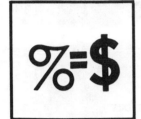

SECTION XI: Interest Problems

SECTION XII: Volume and Circular Area Problems

SECTION XIII: Percentage Problems of Discount and Profit

SECTION XIV: Ratio and Proportion

SECTION XV: Graphs

INTRODUCTION

Mathematics for High School Equivalency Examination presents a series of lessons for the General High School Equivalency Development student which will help him to prepare and successfully pass the G.E.D. test.

Students who study for and take the G.E.D. test have different levels or years of prior schooling. Therefore to help all G.E.D. students the authors have included a Diagnostic Math Test which is at the beginning of this book. Before beginning any of the lessons in this book the student is urged to determine what his (or her) level of ability is. Take the Diagnostic Test on page 3. Then compare your answers with the correct answers given at the back of the book. (Answers for all exercises in this book begin on page 143). After you have done this you will find a listing of the particular mathematical subject area for each question number appearing on the test. Next, use the Math Diagnostic Test Evaluation and find out where you are strong and what, if any, are your weak areas. You can then give your weak areas more study and repeated study as you work through the book.

DIAGNOSTIC MATH TEST

WRITTEN PROBLEMS

1. Which of the following has the least value?
   a) 1/4   b) 33/60   c) 23/100   d) 19/31
   Ans._____

2. Jim walked 1 2/3 miles on Monday, 3 1/7 miles on Tuesday and 1/3 mile on Wednesday. How many miles did he walk in all?
   a) 2 1/3   b) 5 1/7   c) 5 1/3
   d) 4 1/7
   Ans._____

3. What is the product of 4 2/3 times 3 1/2?
   a) 49/3   b) 14/3   c) 24/3
   d) 27/3
   Ans._____

4. 125/300 is the same as:
   a) 3/5   b) 1 3/25   c) 65/150
   d) 5/12
   Ans._____

5. 42/4 is equal to:
   a) 10 3/4   b) 10 1/2   c) 11 1/4
   d) 11 1/2
   Ans._____

6. A store has 120 lamps. If they sell 1/4 of them, how many do they have left?
   a) 90   b) 30   c) 60   d) 100
   Ans._____

7. 1/4, as a percent, is:
   a) 1/4%   b) 25%   c) 75%
   d) 20%
   Ans._____

8. What is the difference between 24/40 and 43/80?
   a) none of these   b) 19/40
   c) 19/80   d) 1/16
   Ans._____

9. Write 5 and 7 hundredths as a decimal.
   a) 5.7   b) 5.07   c) 5.007
   d) none of these
   Ans._____

10. What is 33% of 1200?
    a) 400   b) 40   c) 4   d) 60
    Ans._____

Use the graph below for questions 11 and 12.

FEDERAL BUDGET, ANNUAL AVERAGE: 1967-70

Percent Distribution by Function

RECEIPTS

Corporation Income Tax 19.7

Individual Income Tax 44.9

Employment Taxes Unemployment & Other Insurance & Retirement 22.1

Customs, Estate & Gift Taxes, & Miscellaneous 4.7

Excise Taxes 8.5

3

11. What percent of the total receipts was received from corporation income tax and excise tax?
a) 19.7   b) 44.9   c) 8.5
d) 28.2

Ans._____

12. If the total receipts were $1000, how much
of that was received from excise taxes?
a) $8.50   b) $85   c) $850
d) none of these

Ans._____

13. A man's weekly salary is $50. If he receives
a commission of 5% on his weekly sales and
his sales for one week are $1000, what is his
total salary for that week?
a) $100   b) $105   c) $65
d) $55

Ans._____

14. Mr. Smith borrowed $500 at 6% simple in-
terest. How much must he pay if his loan is
for one year?
a) $506   b) $525   c) $530
d) $515

Ans._____

15. What is 150% of 50?
a) 75   b) 125   c) 100   d) 150

Ans._____

16. If you were making a graph showing the
distribution of income, what graph would
you use?
a) bar graph   b) line graph
c) circle graph   d) vertical bar graph

Ans._____

17. Given the following relationship

F	2	3	4	5
M	6	9	12	

Fill in the missing value for "M".

18.

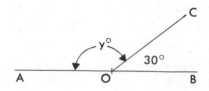

In the figure line segment CO intersects AB
at O. If one angle is 30° then y =
a) 280°   b) 330°   c) 150°
d) 90°

Ans._____

19. The volume of a rectangle is $V = S^2 h$.
Where S is the length of one side of the rectangle and h is the height, what is the volume
when S = 4 and h = 5 ?
a) 80 cubic inches   b) 20 cubic inches
c) 60 cubic inches   d) 16 cubic inches

Ans._____

20. The symbol 4! is read four factorial and
means $4 \cdot 3 \cdot 2 \cdot 1 = 24$. What is the value of
$\dfrac{4!}{2!}$
a) 24   b) 18   c) 12   d) 16

Ans._____

21. Find the quotient when $3 \times^4 + 2 \times^2 + 3 \times$ is divided by $\times^2$.

a) $3 \times^2 + 2 + 3 \times^{-1}$
b) $3 \times^2 + 2 \times + 3 \times$

c) $3 \times^2 + 2 \times + 3 \times^{-1}$
d) $3 \times^2 + 2 + 3 \times$

Ans._____

22. If E, F, G, H are numbers the value of
$\begin{vmatrix} E & F \\ G & H \end{vmatrix}$ is EH − FG what is the value of $\begin{vmatrix} 1 & 2 \\ 3 & 4 \end{vmatrix}$
a) 2   b) −2   c) 0   d) 4

Ans._____

23. The graph below shows the percentage of expenditure for each category. If the total expenditure is $1200, how many more dollars were spent for food than for recreation?

20%	33%	10%	37%
Rent	Food	Recreation	Miscellaneous

    a) $280   b) $400   c) $240
    d) $200

Ans._____

24. What is the next number in this series?
1, 2, 4, 8, ——
    a) 14   b) 16   c) 12   d) 11

Ans._____

25. What is the next number in this series? 1, 3, 7, 15, ——
    a) 21   b) 31   c) 24   d) 19

Ans._____

26. An automobile travels at 50 M.P.H. How long will it take to travel 200 miles?
    a) 160 minutes   b) 40 minutes
    c) 200 minutes   d) 240 minutes

Ans._____

27. The area of a wall is 250 sq. ft. How many gallons of paint must be bought if each gallon covers 30 sq. ft.?
    a) 8 gals.   b) 9 gals.   c) 7 gals.
    d) 6 gals.

Refer to the graph for questions 28 through 30.

28. If (Pn) stands for the total population of Brazil now, then at the end of one year the population will be
    a) P = .035 Pn
    b) P = .035 Pn + Pn
    c) P = .035 Pn − Pn
    d) P = .035 Pn + 2 Pn

Ans._____

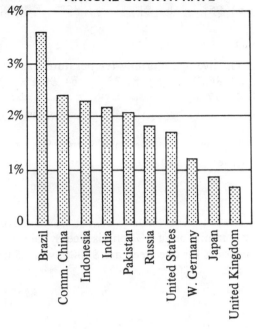

ANNUAL GROWTH RATE

29. Which of the countries has an annual growth rate of approximately 2%?
    a) Indonesia   b) United States
    c) India   d) Pakistan

Ans._____

30. The annual growth rate for Communist China is approximately
    a) .027   b) .024   c) .028
    d) .029

Ans._____

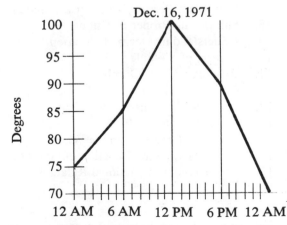

Dec. 16, 1971

The graph shows the temperature variation in a twenty-four-hour period. Refer to it when answering questions 31 through 35.

31. The temperature at 3 AM was approximately
    a) 95°   b) 81°   c) 85°   d) 90°

    Ans._____

32. The average morning temperature was
    a) 86.7°   b) 87.3°   c) 90.1°
    d) 77.6°

    Ans._____

33. The average temperature for the day was
    a) 87°   b) 90°   c) 84°   d) 89°

    Ans._____

34. Which of the following lines of the graph indicate the largest rate of temperature change?
    a) 1   b) 2   c) 3   d) 4

    Ans._____

35. The graph was probably made of a typical day in
    a) the United States   b) South America
    c) Europe   d) can't tell

    Ans._____

MATH PRE-TEST

QUESTION STEM ANALYSIS

Question No.
1. Value of Fractions
2. Addition of Fractions
3. Multiplying Mixed Numbers
4. Reducing Fractions
5. Converting Improper Fractions to Mixed Numbers
6. Multiplying a Fraction and a Whole Number
7. Equivalent Percent Value of a Fraction
8. Subtracting Proper Fractions
9. Understanding Decimal Notation
10. Percent of a Whole
11. Reading a Circle Graph
12. Obtaining Values from a Circle Graph
13. Percent—Commission Problem
14. Percent—Interest Problem
15. Percent—Greater than the Whole
16. Understanding the Function of Graphs
17. Understanding Functional Relationship
18. Recognizing the Concept of 180° in a Straight Line
19. Understanding the Functional Notation of a Formula
20. Ability to Follow Directions
21. The Power Rule for Division
22. Understanding Absolute Value Notation
23. Percent of a Whole
24. Identifying Geometric Progressions
25. Identifying Arithmetic Progressions
26. Rate, Distance, and Time Problem
27. Understanding the Relationship in a Word Problem
28. Establishing Relationship from a Bar Graph
29. Reading a Bar Graph
30. Reading a Bar Graph
31. Reading a Line Graph
32. Determining Average Values
33. Determining Average Values
34. Understanding Line Graphs
35. Inferring Information

MATHEMATICS PRE-TEST EVALUATION

Check yourself by using the following evaluation form. The test is divided into three areas. Listed under each area are the question numbers that correspond to the mathematical operations being tested. Check your answers for each area, then, enter the total number right, in the space provided, in the right-hand column. Compare your score with the total shown.

Area I Basic Operations

Fractions (1, 2, 3, 4, 5, 6, 8)	7
Decimals (9)	1
Percent (7, 10, 12, 13, 14, 15, 23)	7
Total	15

Area II Graphs

Circle (11, 16)	2
Bar (28, 29, 30)	3
Line (31, 32, 33, 34, 35)	5
Total	10

Area III Topical

Relationship (17)	1
Geometry (18)	1
Formulas (19)	1
Factorial (20)	1
Power (21)	1
Notation (22)	1
Series (24, 25)	2
Distance, Rate, Time (26)	1
Area (27)	1
Total	10

Area I, Other Question Items

Formulas	7/7
Decimals	1/1
Percent	5/7

Area II, Other Question Items

Circle	2/2
Bar	3/3
Line	5/5

Area III, Other Question Items

Relationship	1/1
Area	1/1

Evaluation Comments:

Area I . . . If you score less than 13, then you are weak in basic operations.

Area II . . . If you score less than 10, then you are weak in graph reading.

Area III . . . If you score less than 10, then you need to review specific areas that you have missed.

SECTION I
Whole Numbers – Arithmetic Operations

1.0 Addition of Whole Numbers

Addition is the combining of two or more smaller numbers into a larger amount called a sum. Addition examples may appear in number form or written form.

The Addition Table

The addition table shown is organized into vertical columns of numbers and horizontal rows of numbers.

This table shows at a glance how two numbers can be combined to give the sum (or addition) of the two numbers.

For example:

$$4 + 7 = ?$$

First select the vertical column on the left and enter at the number 7 as shown by A.

Second select the top row and enter at the number 4 as shown by B.

Third where the column with the 7 and the row with the 4 meet, at number 11 in this case, is the answer to $4 + 7 = 11$.

This table can help make it easy to add two numbers. Use this table to do (a) of Exercise (1).

General Addition Model

Addition problems which appear on the G.E.D. Test include multiple columns of numbers to be added as well as single columns as in the previous example. A general model for doing addition of columns of numbers is as follows:

add   4741
       6312
      +7849

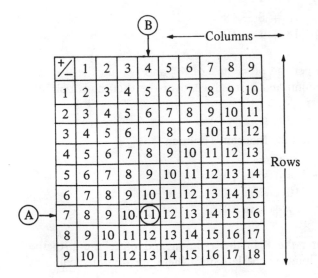

First identify the columns as

① Now add the ones column first as

THINK   1 + 2 = 3, then add
          3 + 9 = 12

But 12 is larger than the ones column therefore enter the *ones place* number of 12 (the 2 in this case) under the ones column; put the 2 under the 9; now put the tens place number of 12 (the 1 in this case) into the tens column. This is called *carrying the number*.

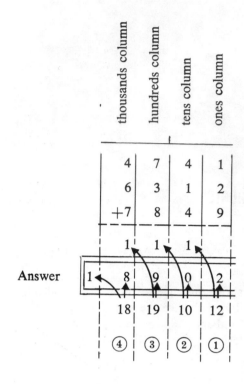

Answer

② Now add the next column, the tens column

THINK   4 + 1 = 5
and   5 + 4 = 9
then   9 + 1 = 10   (the one carried is from the
                          ones column)

As in step ① this number is a two place number rather than a one place number therefore put the last number (the 0) under the column you are adding then carry the next number to the next column as shown by ②.

③ Now add the hundreds column

THINK   7 + 3 = 10
        10 + 8 = 18
        18 + 1 = 19

and as per the procedure of ① and ② put the 9 under this column and carry the 1 over the thousands column.

④ Finally add the thousands column

THINK   4 + 6 = 10
        10 + 7 = 17
        17 + 1 = 18

and enter the 8 in this column and place the 1 in the next column to the left since there are no other columns to add.

(1) Try the following exercise:

Add:

a)
5	3	7	6	7	9	3	4	5	8
+4	+6	+4	+6	+7	+4	+8	+2	+9	+7

b)
17	14	37	72	66	19	23	42	89
+13	+46	+36	+93	+34	+69	+46	+91	+28

c)
312	373	416	443	100	512	729	561
+406	+192	+271	+361	+307	+236	+631	+908

d)
4909	7121	3009	1123	1437	2463	7935
+2633	+8131	+4667	+7272	+1900	+ 600	+1774

(2) Addition examples

Add:

	(a)	(b)	(c)	(d)	(e)
1)	7	8	9	1	2
	6	4	3	4	6
	5	8	9	5	3
2)	16	17	15	27	17
	14	3	9	6	18
	12	18	16	5	86
3)	112	17	25	143	257
	36	108	24	21	311
	8	26	41	8	60
4)	2563	729	305	515	542
	72	8101	183	38	76
	5	31	95	73	35
	811	38	6	11	18

ADD:

5) $63 + 74 + 1{,}306 + 8 =$ _____

6) $79 + 179 + 1179 + 46 =$ _____

7) $119 + 63 + 754 + 83 =$ _____

8) $\$5.04 + \$72 + \$64 + \$5 =$ _____

9) $711 + 32 + 609 + 17 =$ _____

10) $35 + 75 + 609 + 811 =$ _____

When working with word problems the addition sign (+) will not be shown. Instead you will be given *signal words* which mean to add. These words are:

added to	made larger by
increased by	plus
sum	raised by
and	

Addition problems given in words rather than numbers will always include one of these *signal words*.

(3) Now try the following exercise: Be careful to *read the signal words* which mean to add.

a) Five **and** six are _____?

b) Seven **increased by** twenty-six is _____?

c) Eight **added to** one hundred and nine is _____?

d) Thirty-nine **made larger** by seven is _____?

e) John has fifty dollars. If this amount is **raised by** twenty-one dollars, how much money does John have? _____

f) One thousand and ten dollars **increased by** seven hundred and four equals _____?

g) A score of eighty-four **plus** a score of seventy four equals _____?

h) If Mary's weight of one hundred and ten pounds is **increased by** fourteen pounds, how much does Mary weigh now? _____

i) A group of forty **plus** a family of six **plus** a crowd of three hundred and sixty two equals _____?

---

(4) Next try this exercise which is a mix of number problems and word problems.

a) add:

512	331	9	15	46	89	301	78
63	646	8	32	65	77	567	123
9	41	14	57	99	15	472	233

b) 512 plus 46 plus 313 plus 9 equals _____?

c) 66 plus 43 and 96 equals _____?

d) 41 and 39 increased by 71 and 64 equals _____?

e) 76 raised by 32 plus 14 and 19 equals _____?

(5) Answer the following addition questions:

1) Seventeen increased by thirty-five equals what number?

Ans._____

2) What is the sum of seventy-nine and forty-four?

Ans._____

3) The sum of fifteen and nine added to twelve equals what number?

Ans._____

4) One thousand three hundred and four added to seven hundred and forty-one equals what number?

Ans._____

5) Seventy-three made larger by eighty-one equals what number?

Ans._____

6) Eleven hundred and six plus one hundred and nine equals what number?

Ans._____

7) What is the sum of seven, seventy and seven hundred and seventy-one?

Ans._____

8) Forty-seven added to thirteen plus nine equals what number?

Ans._____

9) Six hundred and seventeen plus sixty-six equals what number?

Ans._____

10) Nine plus eight made larger by fifty-one equals what number?

Ans._____

2.0 Subtraction of Whole Numbers

Subtraction is the opposite of addition. Instead of combining two amounts you must take away a smaller sum from a larger sum. The answer is called the *difference*. The subtraction sign is (−).

GENERAL SUBTRACTION MODEL

When there are more than two numbers to subtract the subtraction process is really the same. That is the process works for any amount of number columns. A general model for doing subtraction of columns of numbers is as follows:

subtract   715
         −526

① First identify the columns

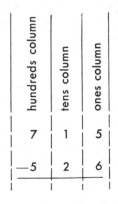

Next expand the multiple numbers of the numerand and subtrahend.

$$
\begin{array}{rl}
\text{numerand } 715 = & 700 + 10 + 5 \\
\text{subtrahend } 526 = & 500 + 20 + 6 \\
\end{array}
$$

THINK 715 is 700 + 10 + 5 = 715
      526 is 500 + 20 + 6 = 526

Now look over step (1a) and note if there are any numbers in the subtrahend which are *larger* than the numerand. There are, the 6 and the 20.

We must increase the numerand 5 by exchanging one of the tens from the ten column and add this to the 5.

THINK 10 + 5 = 15

| 10 added to 5 | Next we increase the tens column by exchanging one of the one hundreds from the hundreds column | 100 added to 0 |

$$700 + 10 + 5 \quad = \quad 700 + 0 + 15 \quad = \quad 600 + 100 + 15$$
$$500 + 20 + 6 \quad = \quad 500 + 20 + 6 \quad = \quad 500 + 20 + 6$$

We do the same procedure for the 20 since we cannot subtract 20 from the 0.

Now we recombine the numbers $100 + 80 + 9 = 189$. This is the answer

We can now carry out our subtraction.

600	100	15
−500	− 20	− 6
100	80	9 ← difference

$$715 \leftarrow \text{numerand}$$
$$-526 \leftarrow \text{subtrahend}$$
$$189 \leftarrow \text{difference}$$

---

(1)   Do the following examples:

a)

9	8	6	5	7	6	4	9	10	14
−5	−3	−4	−1	−6	−2	−1	−7	− 4	− 8

b)

29	36	56	73	91	60	44	53	88
−12	−23	−44	−69	−74	−52	−13	−49	−56

c)

109	124	163	743	700	611	812	936
− 63	−112	−132	−541	−600	−342	−597	−412

d)

1750	1973	1101	6342	10000	9803	5412
− 990	−1562	− 912	−3219	− 8754	−4563	− 981

Word problems for subtractions will not show you the (−) sign. Instead, you will be given *signal words* or *clue words* which mean subtract. These words are:

minus	decreased by	take away
difference	made smaller by	
less than	diminished by	

(2) Try the following word problems:

a) Five thousand decreased by two thousand two hundred and sixteen equals _____?

b) Three hundred and four minus fifty-six equals _____?

c) Sixteen is smaller than twenty-one by _____?

d) The difference between eight hundred and one thousand is _____?

e) The sum of sixteen thousand diminished by five thousand plus six hundred and twelve equals _____?

f) Bill has four hundred and six trading cards. If his supply is decreased by eighty-five cards, how many does Bill now have? _____

g) What is the difference between five hundred dollars and five thousand dollars? _____

h) What is 1973 less twenty-four years? _____

i) How much change do I get from a twenty dollar bill if my groceries cost sixteen dollars? _____

j) A piece of property of three hundred and two acres made smaller by nineteen acres is how large? _____

(3) Subtraction Examples

	(a)	(b)	(c)	(d)	(e)
1)	62 −11	74 −36	88 −81	72 −14	87 −11
2)	60 −58	70 −62	50 −40	73 −37	84 −59
3)	117 − 99	661 −587	421 −311	721 −600	463 − 9
4)	822 −722	800 − 70	721 −155	801 −711	722 −333
5)	703 − 85	3573 −2887	75,006 − 385	8052 −7766	55,092 − 4984

Subtract:

6) $1017 - 642 =$ _____
7) $691 - 546 =$ _____
8) $1724 - 1665 =$ _____
9) $85 - 16 =$ _____
10) $75,363 - 66,594 =$ _____
11) $81,546 - 7,756 =$ _____
12) $8,800 - 7,300 =$ _____
13) $65,000 - 55,005 =$ _____
14) $699 - 569 =$ _____
15) $788 - 96 =$ _____

(4) Answer the following subtraction problems:

1) Five hundred decreased by two hundred and forty-two equals what number?

Ans._____

2) Two thousand and eight minus nine hundred and eighty-four equals what number?

Ans._____

3) What is the difference between sixty-four and twenty-nine?

Ans._____

4) Seventy-six subtracted from one hundred and two equals what number?

Ans._____

5) Eight thousand four hundred and twelve minus four thousand and forty-four equals what number?

Ans._____

6) Five hundred and nineteen taken away from one thousand equals what number?

Ans._____

7) Ten thousand and forty decreased by eighty-six equals what number?

Ans._____

8) Sixty-three diminished by twenty-nine equals what number?

Ans._____

9) Six hundred and forty-two deducted from nine hundred and eight equals what number?

Ans._____

10) The difference between eighty-four and forty-nine equals what number?

Ans._____

3.0 Multiplication of Whole Numbers

Multiplication is the increase in the size of a number by a certain amount of times.

A *times table* is provided for you at the end of this section. You *must* learn your times tables in order to be able to do any more math above this level.

After reviewing or re-learning your times tables, try the examples below. The multiplication sign (×) tells you to multiply the numbers.

(1) Do the following examples:

a)
6	7	6	3	6	8
×9	×3	×8	×3	×0	×1

b)
33	46	17	16	83	66
×9	×8	×9	×14	×12	×51

c)
612	716	808	812	365
× 6	× 17	×903	× 90	×112

Your multiplication answer is called the *product*. Signal words and clue words for multiplication word problems are:

product   multiplied by
times   doubled, tripled

General Multiplication Model

A general model which you can use to work out your multiplication problem answers is as follows:

Multiply   52
       × 26

First note your ones column, and your tens column and so on to any number of columns.

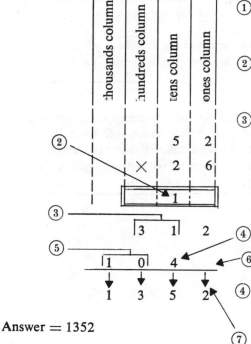

Answer = 1352

(1) Now multiply
THINK $6 \times 2 = 12$
But 12 is too large a number for the ones answer column.

(2) Therefore put the 2 part of the 12 answer into the ones column and carry the 1 part of the 12 into the next column, the tens column as shown by the (2).

(3) Now multiply
THINK $6 \times 5 = 30$
But since we have a 1 which is carried over from step 2, add this 1 to the 30.
    $30 + 1 = 31$
This answer 31 can now be placed next to the 2. Notice that the 1 part of 31 is placed in the tens column and the 3 part into the column to the left, the hundreds column. This step finishes multiplication by the 6 part of the 26 in this problem.

(4) The next step is to multiply by the 2 part of 26.
THINK $2 \times 2 = 4$
Place this answer 4 directly beneath the multiplier 2 part of 26, in the tens column. Notice that the 4 answer here is less than 10. If this answer were more than ten we would have to carry as was done in step (2).

(5) Now finish multiplying by the 2 part of 26
THINK $2 \times 5 = 10$
Place the 10 to the left of the 4, with the 0 part of 10 placed into the hundreds column.

(6) Now add up the products of 6×52 and 2×52.
Notice that there is nothing under the 2, you can place a zero 0 there to make sure you don't lose that place.

(7) Adding now
$2 + 0 = 2$
Bring down the 2 to the answer line
$4 + 1 = 5$
Bring down the 5 to the answer line
$3 + 0 = 3$
Bring down the 3 to the answer line
$1 + 0 = 1$
Notice there was nothing to add the 1 to hence we have
$1 + 0 = 1$
Bring down the 1 in the answer line. The answer is 1352, or in words one thousand, three hundred fifty-two. Notice how the place columns agree with the answer.

(2) Now try the following word problems. Be sure to look for the *signal words* which tell you to multiply.

a) Five times six is _____?
b) The product of forty-five and twelve is _____?
c) One hundred and seventy-four plus fifty multiplied by nine equals _____?
d) Ninety-one times eleven equals _____?
e) Seventeen tripled equals _____?
f) Two hundred and eight doubled equals _____?
g) John has thirty novels and forty short stories. If he triples his supply of literature, how many pieces will he have? _____

h) If Mr. Sanders is given a 9 dollar a week raise, how much extra money will he have after nineteen weeks? _____
i) There are sixteen ounces in a pound. How many ounces are there in twenty pounds ? _____
j) There are three feet in a yard. How many feet are there in sixty-nine yards? _____

> **Note 1**
>
> When you are changing or converting weights or measurements from larger terms to smaller terms (i.e. yards to feet, pounds to ounces, gallons to pints) *always multiply*.

(3) Multiply:

	(a)	(b)	(c)	(d)	(e)
1)	81 × 6	50 × 2	73 × 4	62 × 3	47 × 5
2)	6 × 81	3 × 66	4 × 75	7 × 62	8 × 41
3)	85 × 11	72 × 12	112 × 13	93 × 18	90 × 40
4)	55 × 15	64 × 21	73 × 27	115 × 63	137 × 58

	(a)	(b)	(c)	(d)	(e)
5)	107 × 93	621 × 18	112 × 100	107 × 100	621 × 10
6)	1,000 × 621	1,000 × 72	10,000 × 60	1,750 × 350	8,500 × 311
7)	83 × 317	50 × 500	82 × 750	118 × 1500	712 × 500

8) $55 \times 3 =$ _____
9) $62 \times 11 \times 2 =$ _____
10) $620 \times 11 \times 3 =$ _____
11) $587 \times 5 \times 4 =$ _____
12) $1,000 \times 10 \times 5 =$ _____
13) $10,000 \times 13 \times 6 =$ _____
14) $8 \times 31 \times 150 =$ _____
15) $73 \times 16 \times 9 =$ _____

(4) Answer the following multiplication questions:

1) Sixty-two times seventeen equals what number?

Ans._____

2) One thousand times seventy-four equals what number?

Ans._____

3) What is the product of twenty-four, six and twelve?

Ans._____

4) What number is the equivalent of nine times sixty-four?

Ans._____

5) Five hundred and forty-one times seven equals what number?

Ans._____

6) What is the product of twelve, twenty-four, and thirty-six?

Ans._____

7) Four thousand multiplied by eighteen equals what number?

Ans._____

8) Thirty-six times four times eight equals what number?

Ans._____

TIMES TABLE

1	2	3	4	5	6	7	8	9	10	11	12	13	14	15
2	4	6	8	10	12	14	16	18	20	22	24	26	28	30
3	6	9	12	15	18	21	24	27	30	33	36	39	42	45
4	8	12	16	20	24	28	32	36	40	44	48	52	56	60
5	10	15	20	25	30	35	40	45	50	55	60	65	70	75
6	12	18	24	30	36	42	48	54	60	66	72	78	84	90
7	14	21	28	35	42	49	56	63	70	77	84	91	98	105
8	16	24	32	40	48	56	64	72	80	88	96	104	112	120
9	18	27	36	45	54	63	72	81	90	99	108	117	126	135
10	20	30	40	50	60	70	80	90	100	110	120	130	140	150
11	22	33	44	55	66	77	88	99	110	121	132	143	154	165
12	24	36	48	60	72	84	96	108	120	132	144	156	168	180
13	26	39	52	65	78	91	104	117	130	143	156	169	182	195
14	28	42	56	70	84	98	112	126	140	154	168	182	196	210
15	30	45	60	75	90	105	120	135	150	165	180	195	210	225

Example: $6 \times 5 = ?$

A   Enter table at 6 on the left side.
B   Read down from 5 at the top of table.
C   Read 30 in table, $6 \times 5 = 30$.

4.0 Division of Whole Numbers

In division you are asked to see how many times a smaller number can fit into or be contained in a larger number.

The division sign is (÷). You may also see examples which use the division box, (/‾‾‾‾‾).

The answer to a division problem is called a *quotient*. For example 20 ÷ 5 by using the division box we have:

$$\begin{array}{r} 4 \leftarrow \text{quotient} \\ \text{divisor} \rightarrow 5\overline{)\ 20\ } \text{dividend} \\ \underline{20} \\ 0 \end{array}$$

ART WORK PAGE 46

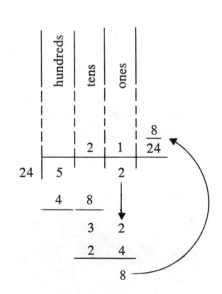

GENERAL DIVISION MODEL

A general model which you can use to work out your division problem answers is as follows:

$$\begin{array}{r} (\text{Answer}) \leftarrow \text{quotient} \\ \text{Divide}\quad 24\overline{)\ 512\ } \end{array}$$

Divisor   Dividend

First note the columns for the dividend.

	Hundreds Column	Tens Column	Ones Column
24	5	1	2

① Now look at the divisor 24, it cannot be divided into the 5 in the dividend since 5 is smaller than 24. Keep counting in the dividend to the right—until you reach a number which 24 will divide into, namely, 51.

THINK is 5 larger than 24 — ans. NO
is 51 larger than 24 — ans. YES

② Divide 24 into the 51.

THINK How many times does 24 go into 51?
Let's try 3 × 20 gives 60, the number 60 is larger than 50 so 3 is too large.
Let's try 2 × 20 gives 40, this number 40 is smaller than 50 so we can use 2 here
Place the 2 in answer directly over the 1 in the tens column.

③ Now multiply 2 × 24 = 48 place the 48 under the 51 and draw a line under the 48.

④ Subtract 48 from 51 = 3 and place the 3 under the 8.

⑤ Bring down the 2 in the ones column, and place next to the 3 to form 32.

⑥ We now repeat the whole process as was done from step ①.

⑦ Look at the 24, how many times does 24 go into 32? Let's try 2 × 24 gives 48, this number is larger than 32. Let's use 1 × 24 = 24, enter the 1 in the ones column and place the 24 under the 32 and draw a line.

⑧ Subtract 24 from 32. The answer is 8.

⑨ Now look at the dividend. Are there any more numbers to be brought down as the 2 was brought down? Answer is NO.

⑩ The 8 therefore is a remainder. Place it over 24 and place 8/24 next to the 21 answer.

---

(1) Do the following examples. Note also that 20/5 tells you to ÷ 20 by 5.

Divide:

a) $20 \div 10$ $55 \div 11$ $62 \div 2$ $77 \div 7$
b) $60 \div 15$ $75 \div 3$ $75 \div 25$ $84 \div 4$
c) $16\overline{)320}$ $15\overline{)4500}$ $12\overline{)2460}$
d) $17\overline{)340}$ $83\overline{)249}$ $102\overline{)1224}$
e) $684 \div 2$ $660 \div 3$ $55 \div 5$ $550 \div 55$

Clue words or signal words for division of whole numbers are these:

quotient   go into
divided by   contained in
                  how many

(2) Try the following exercises:

a) How many five's are there in five hundred and twenty-five? _____

b) How many times can the number six go into six hundred? _____

c) What is the quotient of forty-four and the divisor eleven? _____

d) How many times can sixty-three be divided by 0? _____

e) How many eighteens are contained in five hundred and fifty-eight? _____

f) What is one hundred divided by four? _____

g) If John divides his $124,000 estate into four equal shares, how much will each share be worth? _____

h) How many miles are there in 10,572 feet? _____

i) How many pounds are there in 192 ounces? _____

j) If I have 432 quarts of milk, then how many gallons of milk do I have? _____

Note 2

When changing or converting smaller measures or amounts into larger amounts (i.e. inches to feet, feet to yards) *always divide.*

---

(3) Divide

	(a)	(b)	(c)	(d)
1)	$40\overline{)1600}$	$4\overline{)160}$	$7\overline{)4907}$	$8\overline{)664}$
2)	$9\overline{)900}$	$7\overline{)5250}$	$5\overline{)2755}$	$11\overline{)385}$
3)	$14\overline{)504}$	$27\overline{)702}$	$25\overline{)8075}$	$31\overline{)806}$

(a)	(b)	(c)	(d)
4) $42\overline{)6804}$	$30\overline{)9030}$	$16\overline{)592}$	$15\overline{)705}$
5) $22\overline{)682}$	$40\overline{)32,080}$	$125\overline{)6000}$	$33\overline{)891}$
6) $900 \div 3$	$500 \div 125$	$1000 \div 25$	$40,160 \div 40$
7) $100 \div 5$	$85 \div 85$	$50 \div 5$	$1200 \div 50$
8) $5000 \div 8$	$704 \div 4$	$144 \div 12$	$669 \div 3$

9) What is the quotient of two hundred thirty-four and six?

Ans._____

10) What is the quotient of two thousand five and five?

Ans._____

11) How many thirteens are contained in four hundred and twenty-nine?

Ans._____

12) Six hundred and forty-eight contains how many eights?

Ans._____

13) What is the quotient of five hundred four and twelve?

Ans._____

14) How many twenties are there in forty thousand?

Ans._____

15) How many fours are there in four thousand four hundred forty?

Ans._____

SECTION II
Combinations of Whole Number Operations

In many problems you often must do more than just one operation of addition, or subtraction, or multiplication, or division. These problems are called combination problems. They combine more than one operation before you reach the answer.

For example: 7 plus 9 divided by 4 is _____?

First we add 7 plus 9 (note the signal word 'plus')

$$\begin{array}{r} 7 \\ +\ 9 \\ \hline 16 \end{array}$$

Then we do the next operation, 'divided by 4', (again note the signal word 'divided'). The answer to 7 plus 9 is 16, and 16 is divided by 4

$$4\ \overline{\smash{\big)}\ 16}$$
$$\overset{4}{}$$

which gives the final answer of 4. This problem combined addition and multiplication.

(1) Follow your signal words as they are given in **1.0, 2.0, 3.0,** and **4.0** and find the answer to these word problems:

a) 25 plus 68 and 12 is _____?
b) The sum of twelve and nine divided by three is _____?
c) The difference between 25 times six and 142 is _____?
d) Mr. Messmore makes 108 dollars a week. If his salary is doubled and then diminished by 92 dollars, how much will he make _____?
e) What number is two less than fifteen times eight _____?
f) What is the quotient of 50 and 2 increased by 3 _____?
g) Mr. Martin has 300 leaflets. To show that the hand is quicker than the eye, he doubles them, then triples them, then decreases their amount by 402, then divides the leaflets by 6. How many does he now have _____?
h) Add six and sixty and then subtract fourteen. Now divide by thirteen. What do you have left _____?
i) What is the average of five tests that have grades of 96, 83, 71, 91, 91? _____ (Hint: Average means all the numbers are added together. The total is then divided by how many numbers there are, like 5 in this problem.)
j) The price of eggs is increased from $.98 to $1.07 a dozen. How much more do I pay for 12 dozen eggs _____?

MASTERY TEST I

I ADDITION

1)
$$\begin{array}{r} 9 \\ +4 \\ \hline \end{array}$$

2)
$$\begin{array}{r} 8 \\ +7 \\ \hline \end{array}$$

3)
$$\begin{array}{r} 5 \\ +4 \\ \hline \end{array}$$

4)
$$\begin{array}{r} 3 \\ +6 \\ \hline \end{array}$$

5)
$$\begin{array}{r} 72 \\ +93 \\ \hline \end{array}$$

6)
$$\begin{array}{r} 23 \\ +46 \\ \hline \end{array}$$

7)
$$\begin{array}{r} 42 \\ +91 \\ \hline \end{array}$$

8)
$$\begin{array}{r} 89 \\ +28 \\ \hline \end{array}$$

9)
$$\begin{array}{r} 373 \\ +192 \\ \hline \end{array}$$

10)
$$\begin{array}{r} 443 \\ +361 \\ \hline \end{array}$$

11)
$$\begin{array}{r} 561 \\ +908 \\ \hline \end{array}$$

12)
$$\begin{array}{r} 416 \\ +271 \\ \hline \end{array}$$

13) 512 plus 46 plus 9 =
14) 66 plus 43 and 96 =
15) 41 plus 39 increased by 71 and 64 =
16) 76 raised by 32 plus 14 and 19 =

Total Correct _____

II SUBTRACTION

17) 9 −5

18) 6 −4

19) 14 −8

20) 6 −2

21) 29 −12

22) 36 −23

23) 91 −74

24) 53 −49

25) 109 −23

26) 163 −132

27) 611 −342

28) 936 −412

29) Sixteen less fourteen is

30) The difference between 800 and 1000 is

31) Three hundred and fifty-four minus fifty-six is

32) The result of sixteen diminished by seven is

Total Correct _____

III MULTIPLICATION

33) 6 ×9

34) 5 ×7

35) 8 ×6

36) 7 ×4

37) 16 ×14

38) 22 ×16

39) 83 ×12

40) 66 ×51

41) 716 × 17

42) 812 ×903

43) 365 ×112

44) 612 × 16

45) Five times six is

46) The product of forty-five and twelve is

47) Two hundred and eight doubled is

48) One hundred and seventy-four plus fifty multiplied by nine is

Total Correct _____

IV DIVISION

49) $20 \div 10$ 50) $55 \div 11$ 51) $77 \div 7$ 52) $16 \div 320$

53) $15\overline{)4500}$ 54) $17\overline{)160}$ 55) $102\overline{)224}$

56) $83\overline{)720}$ 57) $507\overline{)6112}$

58) How many fives are there in five hundred and twenty-five? _____

59) How many times does six go into 72? _____

60) How many eighteens are contained in five hundred and fifty-eight? _____

Total Correct _____

V COMBINATION PROBLEMS

61) 25 plus 68 and 12 is _____

62) The difference between 25 times six and 142 is _____

63) What number is two less than fifteen times eight? _____

64) What is the quotient of 50 and 2 increased by 3? _____

65) The difference of 12 and nine divided by three is _____

Total Correct _____

SECTION III
Fractions

Note 3

A *fraction* signifies some part of a whole number. For instance, if a whole is divided among 3 people, each person gets 1/3 of a whole. If a whole is divided among 4 people, each person gets 1/4 of the whole.

Each fraction indicates that the upper or top number, called the *numerator* is being divided by the lower or bottom number, called the *denominator*.

Note 4

The numerator of a fraction shows you how many of the total parts of the whole are present in this particular fraction.

For example:

2/3—There are 3 parts in the whole. The fraction 2/3 represents 2 of the 3 parts.

Note 5

A *proper fraction* has a smaller numerator than denominator—1/2, 1/3, 2/3, 3/4, 3/5, are all proper fractions.

Note 6

An *improper fraction* has a larger numerator than denominator—5/3, 4/3, 3/2, 7/5, 6/4, are all improper fractions.

Note 7

A *mixed number* is a combination of a whole number and a proper fraction 1 2/3, 2 1/2, 3 3/4, 1 1/3, 8 1/4, are all mixed numbers.

Note 8

The denominator of a fraction tells you how many parts there are in the whole.

Note 9

You can treat fractions in the same way you treat whole numbers. You can add, subtract, multiply, and divide fractions.

1.0 Addition of Fractions

In any fraction there is a numerator and denominator, $\dfrac{\text{numerator}}{\text{denominator}}$

Example A. Add 2/7 + 6/7 = ?

① To add fractions you must have a common denominator. In the example both denominators are 7 therefore in this problem the common denominator is 7.

② Now add the numerators.
$2 + 6 = 8$

③ Place the sum, 8, over the common denominator 7 as

$$\frac{2}{7} + \frac{6}{7} = \frac{2+6}{7} = \frac{8}{7}$$

$\dfrac{8}{7}$ is the answer.

④ When the denominator is a smaller number than the numerator as in this problem, 7 is smaller than 8, the 8/7 can be reduced to a form called proper form.

31

⑤ Simply divide as

$$\frac{8}{7} = 7\overline{/8} = 7\overline{/8}\begin{smallmatrix}1\\7\\\hline1\end{smallmatrix} = 7\overline{/8}\begin{smallmatrix}1R1\\7\\\hline1\end{smallmatrix} = 1R1 \quad \text{(or 1 with a Remainder of 1)}$$

$\frac{8}{7} = 1R1 = 1\ 1/7$, $1\ 1/7$ is $8/7$ in proper form.

Example B. Add $\frac{3}{5} + \frac{1}{3} = ?$

① As in example A, establish a common denominator. Choose the lowest number that both 5 and 3 can divide into evenly. This is called the least common denominator.

THINK You cannot use 5, since 3 will not evenly divide into 5. Nor can you use 10 for the same reason. But try 15. 15 will divide both 5 and 3 evenly.

② Now it is necessary to change both fractions into equivalent fractions with the denominator 15.

THINK 5 divides into 15 → 3 times

Now multiply the numerator of $\frac{3}{5}$, 3 by 3　or　$3 \times 3 = 9$ and place the 9 over the common denominator of 15, $\frac{9}{15}$.

THINK 3 divides into 15 → 5 times

Now multiply the numerator of $\frac{1}{3}$, 1 by 5 times or $5 \times 1 = 5$ and place the 5 over the common denominator of 15, $\frac{5}{15}$.

③ Therefore $\frac{5}{3} = \frac{9}{15}$, $\frac{1}{3} = \frac{5}{15}$ and using the common denominator 15

$$\frac{9}{15} + \frac{5}{15} = \frac{9+5}{15} = \frac{14}{15}.$$

④ The fraction $\frac{14}{15}$ cannot be reduced further and is a proper fraction. $\frac{14}{15}$ is the final answer.

---

(1) Change the following improper fractions into mixed numbers or whole numbers:

	(a)	(b)	(c)	(d)					
					4)	21/6	27/2	16/3	15/7
1)	9/5	11/4	3/2	7/3	5)	100/7	91/6	80/7	55/15
2)	6/3	5/3	4/3	3/3	6)	90/6	80/6	75/3	100/3
3)	17/5	17/4	21/3	44/5	7)	100/41	73/23	65/17	87/15

---

(2) Add the Following Fraction Examples:

	(a)	(b)	(c)	(d)	(e)
1)	1/2 +3 1/2	3 1/4 +1 2/4	5 1/6 +3 4/6	8 1/3 +5 2/3	10 1/2 +6 1/2
2)	2 1/2 +1 1/7	3 1/3 +2 1/4	5 2/7 +3 1/5	2 3/4 +3 1/8	5 6/7 +4 3/5

3)　　1 1/2　　　　　2 1/2　　　　　3 3/4　　　　　5 5/6　　　　　10 1/2
　　　　2 1/3　　　　　8 3/4　　　　　1 2/3　　　　　2 2/3　　　　　 6 1/4
　　　 +3 3/4　　　　+5 5/6　　　　+3 1/2　　　　+3 1/3　　　　 +5 2/3

4)　 17 2/7　　　　　22 9/11　　　　25 3/4　　　　　7 1/2　　　　　8 2/3
　　+18 3/10　　　　 +7 1/2　　　　+9 5/6　　　　　6 1/2　　　　　3 3/4
　　　　　　　　　　　　　　　　　　　　　　　　 +5 3/4　　　　 +5 4/5

5)　 16 5/9　　　　　6 11/20　　　　8 7/10　　　　 60 1/4　　　　　7 1/2
　　 +3 2/3　　　　 +5 2/5　　　　　 3/5　　　　　 2 3/4　　　　　8 3/5
　　　　　　　　　　　　　　　　　 + 5/7　　　　 +8 5/6　　　　　+7/8

6)　3/4 + 5 1/2 + 6 7/8 = ____

7)　10 1/2 + 10 1/3 + 10 4/5 = ____

8)　What is the sum of 3/5, 7/8 and 9/16?

9)　6/7 increased by 1 1/4 equals what number?

10)　5 7/8 added to 11 1/3 becomes what number?

11)　6 1/2 plus 5 3/8 plus 3 1/3 equals what sum?

12)　18 2/9 plus 3 1/2 equals what number?

2.0 Mixed Numbers and Improper Fractions

Note 10

　To change a mixed number into an improper fraction, which makes it easier to work with follow these easy steps: (1) multiply the whole number by the fraction denominator, (2) add the numerator to this product, (3) and place this new number over the fraction denominator.

For example: A mixed number is 1 5/7 then

　① 1 × 7 = 7
　② 7 + 5 = 12
　③ place 12 over 7
　　　12/7 is your improper fraction.

Another mixed number is 3 3/5 then

　① 3 × 5 = 15

　② 15 + 3 = 18
　③ place 18 over 5
　　　18/5 is your improper fraction.

Note 11

　To change an improper fraction into a mixed number, which is the best form for your problem answer follow these steps: (1) divide the denominator into the numerator. (2) If you have a remainder, express this remainder as a fraction by placing it over the fraction denominator.

For example:

a)　5/3　① 5 ÷ 3 = 1R2　② R2 place the R2 over the 3, the denominator, as 2/3, 1 2/3 is your mixed number.

b) 19/4 ① 19 ÷ 4 = 4 R3 ② R3 place the R3 over the 4, 3/4, 4 3/4 is your mixed number.

(3) Do the following exercises:

a) Change these mixed numbers into improper fractions:

(1) 4 1/2	(5) 5 1/6	(8) 3 2/7
(2) 3 3/4	(6) 10 2/5	(9) 1 1/9
(3) 7 1/8	(7) 9 1/9	(10) 2 3/5
(4) 11 3/4		

b) Change these improper fractions into mixed numbers:

(1) 17/2	(5) 11/5	(8) 5/4
(2) 26/5	(6) 21/6	(9) 102/19
(3) 8/2	(7) 29/7	(10) 16/6
(4) 9/2		

You may multiply both numbers of a fraction by the same number and not change the value of the fraction.

Example:

$$\frac{1}{2} = \frac{2}{4} = \frac{4}{8} = \frac{16}{32} = \frac{32}{64}$$

Beginning with $\frac{1}{2}$, each fraction has been multiplied by 2, yet each of these fractions is the same value.

You may divide both numbers of a fraction by the same number and not change the value of the fraction.

Example:

$$\frac{16}{24} = \frac{8}{12} = \frac{4}{6} = \frac{2}{3}$$

Each of these fractions has been divided by 2 in both numerator and denominator.

All fractions that are expressed as final answers to a problem must be mixed numbers rather than improper fractions. Change all improper fractions to mixed numbers for answers. Change all mixed numbers to improper fractions in order to work on your fraction problems.

All fractions that are expressed as answers must be reduced. In order to reduce a fraction, you must divide both numerator and denominator by one number which divides into both evenly. Your fraction is fully reduced when you can no longer evenly divide a single number into both numerator and denominator.

Study carefully these model examples.

Model I $\frac{16}{20}$. Can $\frac{16}{20}$ be reduced?

You must determine whether some smaller number can be divided evenly into both 16 and 20.

How about the number 4?

$$\frac{16}{20} \div \frac{4}{4} = \frac{4}{5}$$ $\frac{16}{20}$ can be reduced to $\frac{4}{5}$ by ÷ both the 16 by 4 and the 20 by 4 as shown.

Model II 8/16. Both 8 and 16 can be divided evenly by 4 and 8. You should always use your largest possible divisor. Suppose, however, that you used 4. Then you would get:

$$\frac{8}{16} \div \frac{4}{4} = \frac{2}{4}$$ Notice that this fraction can be further reduced as shown.

$$\frac{2}{4} \div \frac{2}{2} = \frac{1}{2}$$ 1/2 is the final reduced answer.

(4) Reduce these fractions to lowest terms:

a) 4/6 6/8 9/12 20/25 40/45

b) 70/100 20/40 16/18 20/24 8/64

c) 15/20 12/20 10/40 8/10 18/32

d) 20/50 6/9 17/51 13/39 22/55

Now you should be ready for one of the more difficult principles in fractions—the Lowest Common Denominator or LCD.

Many math examples in fractions will contain fractions with the same denominator, for example:

a) $3/4 + 2/4 = 5/4 = 1\ 1/4$
b) $1/3 + 4/3 = 5/3 = 1\ 2/3$
c) $2/7 + 4/7 = 6/7$

In problems like these, *Do Not Add your denominators*—keep them the same.
Add your numerators.

(5) Change these fraction denominators as shown and provide numerators:

a) $\dfrac{3}{5} = \dfrac{}{20}$ $\dfrac{5}{8} = \dfrac{}{16}$ $\dfrac{3}{4} = \dfrac{}{8}$ $\dfrac{2}{5} = \dfrac{}{10}$

b) $\dfrac{7}{8} = \dfrac{}{24}$ $\dfrac{1}{3} = \dfrac{}{9}$ $\dfrac{1}{4} = \dfrac{}{12}$ $\dfrac{1}{5} = \dfrac{}{25}$

c) $\dfrac{3}{7} = \dfrac{}{28}$ $\dfrac{1}{4} = \dfrac{}{64}$ $\dfrac{4}{6} = \dfrac{}{12}$ $\dfrac{1}{9} = \dfrac{}{27}$

---

(6) Add these fractions below. Reduce your answers.

	(a)	(b)	(c)	(d)	(e)
1)	3/4	1/3	1/6	1/5	1/10
	+2/4	+4/3	+4/6	+3/5	+7/10

	(a)	(b)	(c)	(d)
2)	$1/6 + 3/6 =$	$1/4 + 2/4 =$	$1/5 + 4/5 =$	$1/7 + 3/7 =$
3)	$1/9 + 4/9 =$	$1/8 + 5/8 =$	$1/6 + 2/6 =$	$16/18 + 5/18 =$
4)	$5/10 + 3/10 =$	$3/20 + 16/20 =$	$7/9 + 6/9 =$	$16/30 + 12/30 =$

---

(7) Find common denominators and add these fractions. Reduce your answers.

Samples

$$\begin{array}{l} 3/5 = 21/35 \\ +2/7 = 10/35 \\ \hline \quad\ 31/35 \end{array} \qquad \begin{array}{l} 6/7 = 12/14 \\ +1/2 = \ \ 7/14 \\ \hline \quad 19/14 = 1\ 5/14 \end{array}$$

$$\begin{array}{l} 7/10 = 7/10 \\ +1/5\ \ = 2/10 \\ \hline \quad\ \ 9/10 \end{array}$$

	(a)	(b)	(c)	(d)
1)	1/2	5/6	7/8	1/3
	+2/3	+3/4	+1/4	+1/6

2)	2 3/4	3 1/2	2 2/3	4 1/2
	+1 1/6	+4 1/4	+ 1/9	+ 4/7

3)	5 2/3	3 2/9	8 1/2	3 4/15
	+1 5/6	+1 3/5	+3 2/3	+5 3/5

4)	5 1/2	3 1/6	2 2/3	3 5/6
	+1 1/3	+2 2/9	+5 1/4	+1
	2 2/5	5 5/18	1 1/5	2 1/2

5) $3/5 + 5/6 =$

6) $7\ 1/2 + 25/4 =$

(8) Change the following mixed numbers into improper fractions.

	(a)	(b)	(c)	(d)
1)	5 1/2	6 2/3	7 5/8	8 1/2
2)	10 3/4	11 5/6	25 5/7	6 3/20
3)	16 2/3	15 1/2	10 1/5	9 8/9
4)	50 2/3	40 1/3	10 1/4	12 1/5
5)	100 5/6	18 1/9	17 1/5	60 4/5
6)	2 9/11	3 1/3	7 1/9	7 2/9
7)	5 3/5	4 3/5	3 3/5	8 2/13
8)	6 1/6	6 3/10	7 5/13	5 7/15

3.0 Subtraction of Fractions

Note 12

Just as in addition, you must find a common denominator in order to subtract fractions. Again, you must subtract the smaller numerator number from larger numerator number. Keep your denominators the same. In an example like the one below, your top fraction numerator may be smaller than your bottom fraction numerator.

$$\begin{array}{r} 5\ 1/6 \\ -2\ 2/3 \end{array} = \begin{array}{r} 5\ 1/6 \\ -2\ 4/6 \end{array}$$

In a case like this, you must borrow from the whole number. In this example you will need to convert the whole number that you borrow into 6ths. Instead of borrowing 1 whole, you are actually borrowing 6/6.

$$\begin{array}{r} 4\ 1/6 + 6/6 = 7/6 \\ -2\ 4/6 \end{array} \qquad \begin{array}{r} 4\ 7/6 \\ -2\ 4/6 \\ \hline 2\ 3/6 = 2\ 1/2 \end{array}$$

Remember to borrow from the whole number when you must. Remember to reduce all your answers to lowest terms.

(9) Answer the subtraction examples below:

	(a)	(b)	(c)	(d)
1.	2/3 −1/6	5/6 −1/2	3/8 −1/5	5/7 −1/3
2.	4/9 −1/3	5/9 −1/2	3 1/2 −1/3	4 3/4 −2 2/3
3.	5 1/3 −2 2/3	4 1/2 −3 3/4	5 1/2 −3 2/3	6 1/9 −2 1/3
4.	1 7/10 − 3/4	3 3/8 −2 1/2	3 5/6 −3	5 1/9 −4 3/4

5.   2 3/4 − 1 5/6 =

6.   7 1/8 − 3 3/8 =

(10) Subtract:

	(a)	(b)	(c)	(d)	(e)
1)	5 2/3 −1 1/3	8 3/4 −6 1/4	9 5/6 −1 1/6	7 3/5 −4 1/5	3 9/10 −2 3/10
2)	6 1/2 −3 1/4	8 2/3 −5 1/6	10 5/7 −3 1/3	11 5/9 −10 1/2	18 6/7 −4 3/4
3)	19 9/10 −6 3/7	1 1/2 − 7/8	5 −3 1/2	12 2/3 −5 7/8	18 17/20 −8 3/5
4)	7 1/4 −3 2/5	3 1/6 −2 2/5	5 5/7 −4 1/2	10 2/5 − 7	11 3/7 − 5

5) $6\ 1/2 - 3\ 3/4 = $ _____

6) $7\ 3/8 - 5\ 7/8 = $ _____

7) $10\ 8/9 - 9\ 1/9 = $ _____

8) $7\ 1/3 - 7\ 1/4 = $ _____

9) $11\ 1/6 - 5\ 5/6 = $ _____

10) $1\ 1/12 - 9/10 = $ _____

11) What is the difference between 15 and 9 7/8?

12) 16 1/4 decreased by 6 9/10 equals what number?

13) 14 5/7 diminished by 3 5/6 equals what number?

14) 12 minus 7 4/9 equals what number?

15) 16 3/8 minus 8 equals what number?

---

(11) Addition and subtraction of fractions—verbal problems

1. A business concern is divided among three partners. The first partner owns 1/2 of the industry, and the second partner owns 1/8 of the industry. How much does the third person own?

2. Which is larger, 5/8 or 17/20?

3. How much is left of a 10 2/3″ strip of ribbon after 5 8/9″ have been used?

4. John is 6 ft. 3 1/2 inches tall. Phillip is 5 ft. 10 3/8 inches tall. What is their combined height? How much taller is John than Phillip?

5. Ben threw a shot put 58 ft. and 5 3/4 inches, 61 ft. 4 5/9 inches, and 59 ft. 1/6 inches. What was the total of Ben's three throws?

6. On one day Harry walked 1/2 mile in the morning, 5/9 mile in the afternoon and 1 7/12 mile in the evening. The next day, Harry walked 2 2/3 miles. Did Harry walk further on the first day or the second day? By how much?

7. Lucille was 5 ft. 6 2/3 inches tall. In January, she grew 1/4 inch. In February, she grew 3/8 inch. How tall is she now?

8. Four men split travel expense. The first pays 1/2, the second pays 1/6, the third pays 1/6. How much does the fourth man pay?

4.0 Multiplication of Fractions

Multiplying fractions is easier than adding or
subtracting fractions, because in multiplication
you will not need to find a common denominator.

Note 13

In order to multiply fractions, you
multiply the numerator times numerator and the denominator times denominator. The result will be your new
fraction. For example:

a. $1/2 \times 2/3$ $\dfrac{1 \times 2}{2 \times 3} = \dfrac{2}{6}; \dfrac{2}{6} = \dfrac{1}{3}$

b. $3/5 \times 1/7$ $\dfrac{3 \times 1}{5 \times 7} = \dfrac{3}{35}$

c. $2/7 \times 1/3$ $\dfrac{2 \times 1}{7 \times 3} = \dfrac{2}{21}$

d. $3/2 \times 4/5$ $\dfrac{3 \times 4}{2 \times 5} = \dfrac{12}{10};$

$\dfrac{10}{12} = 1\dfrac{2}{10} = 1\dfrac{1}{5}$

In example d, the numerator in the answer was
larger than the denominator. You must divide
the denominator into the numerator and place
your remainder over the denominator. In other
words, change your improper fraction into a
mixed number as shown in example d. As you
are doing the work for your examples, you
should change mixed numbers into improper
fractions. When you get your answer, change
them back again.

---

(12) Do the multiplication examples and problems below. Reduce your answers.

	(a)	(b)	(c)	(d)
1.	$2/3 \times 5/6$	$3/8 \times 2/9$	$5/2 \times 1/2$	$1\,3/4 \times 5/6$
2.	$3/8 \times 1/7$	$5/3 \times 3/7$	$3\,2/3 \times 1\,5/9$	$1/6 \times 1/5$
3.	$5/9 \times 2/7$	$6/2 \times 1/3$	$7/2 \times 1/5$	$5/6 \times 3/8$

The word 'of' means multiply. It is used in both number and verbal problems.

4. $1/2 \times 3/9 =$ $2/3$ of $7/2 =$ $6/5$ of $3\,1/2 =$ $1/7$ of $8/3 =$

All whole numbers should be expressed, in your
examples, with a denominator of 1.

For example:

$2 = 2/1$ $3 = 3/1$ $4 = 4/1$ $5 = 5/1$
$6 = 6/1$ etc.

Once you obtain your answer you may drop the
denominator of 1. For example:

a) $1/2$ of $8 = 1/2 \times 8/1 = 8/2 = 4$
b) $1/4$ of $24 = 1/4 \times 24/1 = 24/4 = 6$

(13) Do the following problems:

1. $1/5$ of $25 =$ $1/7$ of $46 =$ $3/5$ of $15 =$

2. $2/7$ of $14 =$ $5/8$ of $64 =$ $7/5$ of $25 =$

3. What is $1/3$ of $3/5$?

4. What is $3/7$ of 140 dollars?

5. A trip to Massachusetts takes $3\,2/3$ hours.
    How much time does $1/3$ of the trip take?

6. How much is $1/5$ of 16 years?

7. What is $1/3$ of $24\,2/3$ acres?

8. New York to Buffalo is 400 miles. Laurie
    drives $1/3$ of the way. Tommy drives $1/6$ of
    the way. Eddie drives $1/2$ of the way. How
    far does each person drive?

(14) Multiplication of Fractions—Additional examples

1) $5/8 \times 1/2 =$ _____

2) $2/3 \times 1/4 =$ _____

3) $5/9 \times 1/3 =$ _____

4) $3/4 \times 2/9 =$ _____

5) $3/10 \times 1/6 =$ _____

6) $5/8 \times 6 =$ _____

7) $3/4 \times 12 =$ _____

8) $16 \times 1/4 =$ _____

9) $9/10 \times 3/2 =$ _____

10) $8/3 \times 3/8 =$ _____

11) $1/7 \times 7 =$ _____

12) $5/3 \times 3/5 =$ _____

13) $6\ 1/2 \times 4/7 =$ _____

14) $3\ 1/3 \times 5/7 =$ _____

15) $2\ 1/5 \times 8 =$ _____

16) $3\ 1/5 \times 7 =$ _____

17) $1\ 1/5 \times 3\ 1/8 =$ _____

18) $2\ 1/3 \times 8\ 1/2 =$ _____

19) $17/20 \times 4\ 2/3 =$ _____

20) $11/2 \times 6\ 1/8 =$ _____

21) $3\ 1/8 \times 5\ 1/2 =$ _____

22) $8 \times 8/2 =$ _____

23) $7/5 \times 5\ 1/7 =$ _____

24) $9/5 \times 3\ 1/2 =$ _____

25) What is 2/3 of 12?

26) What is 8/7 of 26?

27) What is the product of 7/3 and 9/10?

28) What is the product of 3/4 and 5 3/10?

29) If 3/8 of a class of 64 students failed a test, how many students failed the test?

30) 7/8 of 3 3/4 lbs. is how many pounds?

31) 3/4 of a 440 yd. run is a distance of how far?

32) 1/3 of 6 1/2 miles is a distance of how far?

5.0 Division of Fractions

Division of fractions is performed the same as multiplication *except* that the second fraction—the fraction after the division sign, the divisor—is inverted. After inverting, the problem then is identical to ordinary multiplication of fractions as in the prior section. Do not invert both fractions. <u>Only the divisor.</u> Once you have inverted your divisor, you must change the division sign to a multiplication sign. Next you multiply to get your answer.

For example:	Step ① Invert Divisor	Step ② Sign Change; Problem Becomes	Step ③ Answer
$1/2 \div 3/8$	8/3	$1/2 \times 8/3 = \dfrac{1 \times 8}{2 \times 3} =$	$8/6 = 1\ 1/3$
$1/3 \div 1/4$	4/1	$1/3 \times 4/1 = \dfrac{1 \times 4}{3 \times 1} =$	$4/3 = 1\ 1/3$
$1/5 \div 2/3$	3/2	$1/5 \times 3/2 = \dfrac{1 \times 3}{5 \times 2} =$	$3/10$

Remember to ① invert divisor fraction, ②
change sign from division to multiplication, and
③ reduce your answer.

---

(15) Do the division problems below:

	(a)	(b)	(c)	(d)
1.	$1/2 \div 1/4$	$3/2 \div 2/3$	$3 \div 1/5$	$3/7 \div 1/3$
2.	$3/4 \div 7/9$	$3/7 \div 5/7$	$5/8 \div 3/11$	$1/10 \div 1/5$
3.	$5 \div 3/2$	$7 \div 4\ 2/3$	$5/9 \div 2\ 1/6$	$11/12 \div 5/14$
4.	$2\ 1/5 \div 3/2$	$5/6 \div 2/5$	$6\ 1/6 \div 5/3$	$4\ 1/2 \div 5$

5. Divide 39 2/5 acres between 2 people.

6. How many 2/3's are there in 16 1/2?

7. Divide a work chore of 6 3/5 hours among 4 people. How much work must each person do?

8. How many 3 1/2's are there in 5/8?

9. Three people must split 4/7 of a pie. How much of the pie will each get?

10. Which is larger? 3/5 of 16 or $16 \div 3/5$?

11. How many 1/3's are contained in 5 1/2?

12. How many 3/4's are contained in 16 7/8?

---

(16) Division of Fractions—Additional examples

1) $1/4 \div 1/3 =$ _____   2) $5/6 \div 1/6 =$ _____   3) $3/4 \div 3/4 =$ _____

4) $6/7 \div 2/7 =$ _____   5) $3/10 \div 1/4 =$ _____   6) $10/3 \div 1/4 =$ _____

7) $9/2 \div 7/8 =$ _____   8) $3/5 \div 3/2 =$ _____   9) $9/10 \div 3/2 =$ _____

10) $8/9 \div 1\ 1/2 =$ _____   11) $3/5 \div 5/3 =$ _____   12) $8/9 \div 2\ 1/2 =$ _____

13) $5/7 \div 2 =$ _____   14) $4 \div 3/4 =$ _____   15) $7/10 \div 6 =$ _____

16) $3/5 \div 3/4 =$ _____   17) $11\ 5/6 \div 3\ 1/8 =$ _____   18) $3\ 1/3 \div 10\ 1/2 =$ _____

19) $5\ 1/4 \div 8 =$ _____   20) $3\ 1/2 \div 5 =$ _____   21) $4\ 2/3 \div 2/3 =$ _____

22) $3\ 1/16 \div 5 =$ _____   23) $7/8 \div 2/3 =$ _____   24) $7/2 \div 8/3 =$ _____

---

25) How many 2/3's are there in 6?

26) How many 3/5's are there in 20?

27) How many 5/3's are contained in 15?

28) $\dfrac{\frac{2}{3}}{\frac{3}{4}}$ 29) $\dfrac{5/6}{7/8}$ 30) $\dfrac{5\ 1/2}{3}$ 31) $\dfrac{7\ 2/9}{5\ 1/3}$

32) How many 3/5 inch strips of ribbon are in 100 inches of ribbon?

33) How many 3/4 mile sections are there in 24 miles of road?

34) How many 6/7 gallons are there in 14 gallons of liquid?

SECTION IV
Decimals and
Decimals to Fractions

Observe the following arrangement of numbers and columns.

	thousands	hundreds	tens	ones	.	tenths	hundredths	thousandths	ten thousandths
1.	5	4	3	2	.				
2.		3	8	3	.				
3.		3	6	4	.	2			
4.			6	5	.	2	6		
5.		1	2	3	.	2	6	7	

Note 13.1

Decimals are parts of a whole that are arranged in columns, just like whole numbers. The decimal point (.) tells you that the number you are reading is a decimal and not a whole number.

The first column to the *right* of the decimal point is the *tenths* column. Note that 5,432 is a whole number on the table above. There is no decimal point in this number. Therefore, there is not a decimal number present after the 2.

383 is the next number. Is there a decimal here? No, 383 represents a whole number without a decimal number.

Now look at the third number. It looks like this:

364.2 364 and how many tenths? 364 and 2 tenths.

The second column to the right of the decimal point is the *hundredths* column. The third column to the right is the *thousandths* column. The fourth column is *ten thousandths*. The fifth column is *hundred thousandths*. Each of the columns to the right is ten times smaller than the last column. Decimal number columns therefore decrease in the number value as they are traced from left to right of the decimal point. 65.26 is read sixty-five and twenty-six hundredths. 123.267 is read one hundred twenty-three and two hundred sixty-seven thousandths. Be careful to read the correct decimal name for the number.

Note 14

Zeroes may be added to the end of a decimal number without affecting the value of the number. For example:

3.4 = 3.40 = 3.400 = 3.4000
6. = 6.0 = 6.00 = 6.000

Note 15

Often in decimal examples you will be asked to round your decimals off. Some decimals would continue endlessly if they were not rounded off.

If you are asked to round off in a certain column, you must look to the column to the right of the column you are rounding off.

For example, 2.67

If you wish to round off this decimal to the nearest tenth you must locate the tenths column. There are six tenths. Look to the column to the right of the tenths. If the number there is 5 or more, raise your six tenths to seven tenths. If the number there is less than 5, then you must keep the 6 in the tenths column. Your number stops at the place of rounding off.

Notice these examples in rounding off:

1.03   2.47   .64   .83   .48   .69

Round these numbers off to the nearest tenth. Your answers should look like these:

1.0   2.5   .6   .8   .5   .7

1.0 Addition of Decimals

In order to add decimals you must make vertical columns, making sure that all of your decimal points are in line as shown in these examples:

```
  2.6          35.6          .006
  .04          .55           .6
  .3           .02          5.8
 ____         ____          ____
```

Notice how all of the decimal points are in a vertical line. Once you have done this, proceed to add the numbers and carry your decimal point straight down into your answer. You may add zeroes after the last digit in a decimal number as a place holder as shown.

```
  2.60         35.60         .006
  .04          .55           .600
  .30          .02          5.800
 _____        _____         _____
  2.94         36.17        6.406
```

Remember to keep your decimal columns in line.
(1)   Do the addition examples below:

	(a)	(b)	(c)	(d)
1.	3.6	3.8	17.2	308.60
	.5	.9	6.8	35.13
	.72	.51	5.3	

	(a)	(b)	(c)	(d)
2.	15.03	5.3	7.23	6.9
	6.17	.76	.81	5.3
	7.99	.09	5.3	.66

3. Add:

   a. .56 + .7 + 13.8
   b. 16 + 18.1 + 26.23
   c. .16 + .181 + 2.623

   d. 19.2 + 100.7 + .67
   e. 26 + 33.33 + 8.76
   f. 39.7 + 42.08 + 69.0
   g. 82.3 + 82.6 + 8.26
   h. 1.23 + 12.3 + 123.0

4. Which is larger?   .49 or .60?
                       3.17 or 3.2?
                       3.0999 or 3.1?

5. Round these numbers off to the nearest *hundredths*:

(a)	(b)	(c)	(d)
3.067	5.009	7.666	8.505
5.323	.079	.061	.136

6. Add 25¢ and 69¢ and 47¢ using decimals.

7. How much is a grocery bill for these items?

   meat @ $1.67
   bread @ $.49
   soda @ $1.09
   vegetables @ $1.95

To change a fraction into a decimal divide the fraction denominator into the numerator.

Example: 2/5, $5/\overline{2.0}$, $5/\overline{2.0}$, then $\frac{2}{5} = 0.4$

$$\begin{array}{r} 0.4 \\ \hline 5/2.0 \\ 2.0 \\ \hline 0 \end{array}$$

(2)   Change the following fractions to decimals. Round off your answer to the nearest hundredth where necessary:

1)	1/2	2)	1/4	3)	3/10
4)	1/3	5)	5/7	6)	9/10
7)	4/5	8)	2 2/7	9)	3 1/8
10)	1 1/2	11)	3/5	12)	1/7

(3)   Decimals—additional examples:

1)	.72	2)	.37	3)	.17	4)	9.2
	.31		.09		3.08		.25
	.40		.11		2.10		31.05

5)	.62	6)	1.11	7)	3.73	8)	.05
	5.81		.027		5.88		7.1
	4.32		3.03		.91		37.742

9)	.003	10)	71.2	11)	.162	12)	7.3
	.03		80.5		.53		.8
	.3		7.72		6.257		1.00

13) $.08 + .17 + 3.42 =$ _____

14) $3.87 + 6.11 + 2.0 =$ _____

15) $.62 + 8.5 + .0723 =$ _____

16) $11.2 + 13.13 + 8.8 =$ _____

17)   .7 mile increased by .5 mile equals how many miles?

18) $5.43 plus an additional $7.12 is how much money?

19)   3.52 added to 7.52 equals what number?

2.0 Subtraction of Decimals

Subtraction of decimals also requires that you line up your decimal points and columns. Once you have done that, subtract the smaller number from the larger number.

(4)   Do these examples:

	(a)	(b)	(c)	(d)
1.	16.37	5.88	3.672	.932
	− 4.60	−3.79	−2.003	−.64
2.	203.7	66.66	78.36	350.72
	−115.8	−55.55	−39.88	−195.55

3.   Subtract:

a. $16.64 − 3.973$

b. $26.5 − 14.60$

c. $7.8 − 3.2$

d. $78.86 − 62.97$

e. $58.9 − 33.7$

f. $63.9 − 32.05$

g. $7.641 − 3.926$

h. $182.62 − 181.99$

4.   What is the difference between 69.7 and 38.9?

5.   What is the difference between 35.62 and 107.4?

6.   How much further is 307.62 miles than 163.97 miles?

7. A man with 11,000 dollars spends $609.37 and $42.67 and $5,032.64 on expenses. How much money does he have left?

8. A bill for sporting goods comes to $62.73. How much change is there from a hundred dollar bill?

9. A budget of $10.9 billion is divided among Education, Defense and Social Services. $5.23 billion is labelled for Education. $1.73 billion is given over to Social Services. How much money is left for Defense?

10. How much less than one minute is a running time of 57.63 seconds?

(5) Decimals—additional examples

1)	5.8 -3.2	2)	7.4 -5.1	3)	.9 $-.3$

4)	8.1 -7.0	5)	9.8 -3.3	6)	11.3 -8.1

7)	12.2 -8.6	8)	8.0 -6.7	9)	10 -5.5

10)	9.23 -8.07	11)	7.8 -5.1	12)	653.72 -77.08

13)	37.32 -11.77	14)	5.37 -1.01	15)	37 -3.6

16)	37.6 -8.2	17)	53.16 -40.30	18)	6.66 -3.37

19)	30 -29.2	20)	15.1 -3.9

21) 66.05 diminished by 30.8 equals what number?

22) 29 decreased by 26.52 equals what number?

23) 36.2 minus 17.7 equals what number?

24) $50.00 is how much greater than $42.88?

25) A time of 10.2 seconds is how much faster than a time of 13.1 seconds?

3.0 Multiplication of Decimals

In order to multiply decimals, you do not have to line your decimal points up. You must pay attention to the decimal numbers in your problem. Multiply one number times the other number to find your answer as shown:

$$
\begin{array}{r}
3.96 \\
\times\ 3.2 \\
\hline
792 \\
1188 \\
\hline
12672
\end{array}
$$

In order to determine where your decimal point should be placed, you must count the number of decimal numbers in your problem (*not whole numbers*, not the numbers to the left, only those numbers to the right of the decimal points). There are three decimal places in the above example. Count off three places from the last number at the right of your answer. After counting off three places to the left of this number, place your point there.

For example

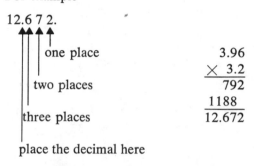

$$
\begin{array}{r}
3.96 \\
\times\ 3.2 \\
\hline
792 \\
1188 \\
\hline
12.672
\end{array}
$$

place the decimal here

Notice these sample examples:

a.
$$
\begin{array}{r}
3.7 \\
.3 \\
\hline
1.11
\end{array}
$$
b.
$$
\begin{array}{r}
36.1 \\
.22 \\
\hline
722 \\
722 \\
\hline
7.942
\end{array}
$$
c.
$$
\begin{array}{r}
10 \\
.112 \\
\hline
20 \\
10 \\
10 \\
\hline
1.120
\end{array}
$$
d.
$$
\begin{array}{r}
.06 \\
.122 \\
\hline
12 \\
12 \\
06 \\
\hline
.00732
\end{array}
$$

Note 15.1

In sample 'd', there were 5 decimal places in the example. There were only 4 decimal numbers in the answer. In cases like this *zeroes are added in front of the decimal answer*. One zero had to be added in sample 'd' in order to count 5 places from the right end of the number in the answer.

(6) Do the multiplication problems below:

1. (a)   (b)   (c)   (d)

3.72	.37	57.3	3.31
× .5	× .2	× .61	× .4

2.

15.6	.012	.573	36.3
× .33	× .1	× 32	× 12

3.

56.3	5.63	5.63	.563
× 10	× .10	×100	× .1

	(a)	(b)	(c)	(d)
4.	66.2 × 10	67.3 × .11	.73 ×.01	.832 × .1
5.	.735 × .2	.675 × 3.8	3.9 ×3.9	583 × .71

6. If one can of peas costs $.29, how much do you pay for a dozen cans?

7. Gas costs 42.9 per gallon. How much does 10 gallons cost?

8. A car averages 19.72 miles per gallon of gas. How far can the car go on 21 gallons of gasoline?

9. A man pays $57.35 a week for rent. How much does he pay in a year?

10. A man runs a mile in 4.75 minutes. How long will it take him to run 5.7 miles?

(7) Decimal multiplication—additional problems

1) 7.1 × .8   2) .2 ×.6   3) .3 × 5   4) .32 × 10   5) .61 × 10

6) .77 ×5.2   7) 3.2 ×5.9   8) 62.3 × .4   9) .032 × 11   10) 11.3 × 6.2

11) .027 × 10   12) 31.6 × 22   13) 3.71 × .9   14) 12.3 × 5.7   15) 300.2 × 1.6

16) 62.5 × .55   17) 81.1 × 33   18) .39 ×1.6   19) 21.1 × 37   20) 82.3 × .01

21) What is .72 of 32.5?
22) What is .9 of 18?
23) What is 7.2 times 8.5?
24) What is the product of 17.3 and 6.6?

25) What number is 3.2 times as great as 10.5?
26) What is 3.2 times $62.50?
27) What is the product of 7.5 and 19.3?

4.0 Division of Decimals

In order for decimals to be divided properly, the decimal point in the divisor must be moved to the right so that the divisor becomes a whole number. However for every place that the decimal point is moved in the divisor, the decimal point must also be moved the same number of places in the dividend. Notice the following example:

quotient   201.
divisor$\overline{\text{dividend}}$ .25.$\overline{)50.25.}$

> **Note 15.2**
>
> If there are no more places to move your decimal point in your dividend, then you add a zero after the dividend number, to the right, for each space you move.

The decimal point in .25 must be moved two places in order to divide properly. Because you moved your decimal point two places in your divisor, you also must move your decimal point two places in the dividend.

Notice this example:

                    3000
.003$\overline{)\ 9}$ .003.$\overline{)\ 9.000.}$

---

(8) Decimal division—
Round off to nearest tenth where necessary

1) .03$\overline{)6.6}$ 2) .82$\overline{)52.72}$ 3) .16$\overline{).6416}$

4) .23$\overline{).0690}$ 5) .11$\overline{)77.22}$ 6) 5.1$\overline{)102}$

7) 1.5$\overline{)50.10}$ 8) .07$\overline{)4.9}$ 9) .003$\overline{)7.4240}$

10) .61$\overline{)35.99}$ 11) 1.3$\overline{)39.26}$ 12) .071$\overline{)542.8}$

13) $\dfrac{.1120}{.31}$ 14) $\dfrac{.621}{1.5}$ 15) $\dfrac{62.53}{2.4}$

16) $\dfrac{54.60}{6}$ 17) $\dfrac{62.5}{.5}$ 18) $\dfrac{18.0}{4.5}$

19) $\dfrac{40.2}{.6}$ 20) $\dfrac{18.90}{3}$ 21) 60.6 ÷ .6

22) 100 ÷ .10   23) 7.5 ÷ 2.5   24) 900 ÷ .03

25) .620 ÷ 62   26) How many .75 are there in 100?

27) How many .25 are there in 50?   28) What is the decimal equivalent of 4 divided by 7?

29) How many 6.2's are there in 40?

(9)   Percent Examples—Additional Problems

I.   Change the following decimals into percents

1) .50	2) .25	3) .33	4) .66	5) .70
6) .2	7) .3	8) .7	9) .8	10) .9
11) .125	12) .065	13) .08	14) .09	15) .011
16) 1.23	17) 3.50	18) 5.00	19) 1	20) 4

II.   Compute the following percentages

21)   What is 20% of 130?   22)   What is 60% of 50?

23)   What is 15% of 40?   24)   What is 120% of 200?

25)   What is 85% of 25?   26)   What is 42% of 84?

27)   What is 300% of 15?   28)   What is 57% of 112?

5.0 Rounding Off Decimals

Often you will be asked to take a decimal which is long or a decimal which is continuous and round it off to a certain number of places. If you are asked to round off to the nearest tenth you must locate the number in the tenths column.

For example:

┌──── tenths column
│ ┌──── hundreds column
↓ ↓
3.834 , 3.⑧34

After doing this, locate the number immediately to the right of the place at which you are rounding off. In this case, you would look to the hundredths column. If the number there is less than 5, eliminate all numbers beyond the tenths column as it stands. In our example:

3.⑧③4 rounds off to 3.8

If the number to the right of the tenths column is 5 or more, eliminate all numbers to the right of the tenths column and raise the tenths column digit one number. For example:

3.⑤7   3.⑤⑦ rounds off to 3.6

(10)   Round off the following decimals to the nearest tenth:

(a)	(b)	(c)	(d)	(e)
3.62	.76	1.33	7.64	8.08

(11)   Round off to the nearest hundredth:

(a)	(b)	(c)	(d)	(e)
3.624	5.8882	6.032	4.111	.0054

(12)   Round off to the nearest thousandth:

(a)	(b)	(c)	(d)	(e)
.05832	.7743	.03945	8.8084	5.0632

(13)   Divide the following decimals. Round off, where necessary, to the nearest hundredth. Add zeroes to the right of your decimal points in order to carry your answer into decimals.

	(a)	(b)	(c)	(d)
1.	.06/͞3͞6͞.͞0͞6	.5/͞2͞5͞.͞1͞5	.8/͞6͞0͞.͞0	.17/͞3͞.͞4͞0͞0

2.	1.8 ÷ .3	1.8 ÷ .003	72 ÷ 20.6	54.0 ÷ .6
3.	.72 ÷ .18	570 ÷ 28.5	66 ÷ 1.1	56 ÷ 6.6
4.	.72 ÷ 9	660 ÷ 2.2	8.8 ÷ 16	.04 ÷ 2.2

5. How many .5's are there in 15.75?

6. How many .7-inch strips can be cut from a 49-inch length of ribbon?

7. A 12-foot tree is cut in .4-foot sections. How many whole sections can be cut off?

8. How many .5-foot sections of rope are there in 116 inches of rope?

9. How many .9-inch sections of watermelon can be cut from a 16-inch watermelon?

6.0 Changing Fractions to Decimals

In order to change a common fraction to a decimal fraction, you must divide the numerator by the denominator. Place a point after the numerator and carry the decimal division to as many places in the quotient as you like. Note the examples below:

$\frac{1}{5}$ = ? decimal

$$\frac{1}{5} \longrightarrow 5/\overline{1}. \quad \text{add decimal point}$$

$$5/\overline{1.0} \longleftarrow \text{then add zeros}$$

$$\begin{array}{r} .2 \\ 5/\overline{1.0} \\ \underline{10} \end{array}$$

$\frac{1}{4}$ = ? decimal

$$\begin{array}{r} .25 \\ 4/\overline{1.00} \\ \underline{8} \\ 20 \end{array}$$

If your decimal quotient is not even, you must round off to the decimal place called for in the problem.

	(a)	(b)	(c)	(d)
2.	$\frac{3}{2}$	$\frac{5}{4}$	$\frac{8}{10}$	$\frac{5}{5}$

(15) Change the following fractions to decimals. Round off to nearest hundredth.

	(a)	(b)	(c)	(d)
1.	$\frac{3}{8}$	$\frac{5}{6}$	$\frac{7}{8}$	$\frac{5}{9}$
2.	$\frac{8}{5}$	$\frac{4}{7}$	$\frac{9}{11}$	$\frac{2}{3}$

(14) Change the following fractions to decimals.

	(a)	(b)	(c)	(d)
1.	$\frac{1}{2}$	$\frac{3}{4}$	$\frac{3}{5}$	$\frac{2}{5}$

SECTION V
Changing Decimal Fractions to Common Fractions

To change a decimal into a fraction, you must note the place that the decimal is carried to. If your decimal is in tenths, you must place your decimal over a denominator of ten. If your decimal is in hundredths, you must place your decimal over a denominator of 100, and so on with thousandths, ten thousandths, etc. Note these examples:

$$.5 = \frac{5}{10} = \frac{1}{2} \qquad .75 = \frac{75}{100} = \frac{3}{4} \qquad .800 = \frac{800}{1000} = \frac{4}{5}$$

(1) Express these decimals as fractions. Reduce when possible.

	(a)	(b)	(c)	(d)
1.	.16	.8	.175	.45
2.	.35	.04	.17	.006
3.	.72	.56	.44	.036

4. Which is larger?

   a. 3/4 or .73?
   b. 5/6 or .88?
   c. 1/12 or .06?
   d. 5/8 or .6?
   e. 2/3 or .64?
   f. .7 or 8/9?

5. Determine the fractional and decimal part (to the nearest hundredth) of total games that each of these basketball teams won.

	Won	Lost
Boston	72	43
New York	65	50
Atlanta	61	54
Baltimore	45	70
Kansas City	20	95

SECTION VI
Percents

The arithmetic of percents is based on hundredths. *For example* $1\% = 1/100$. *If a student were to correctly answer 78 questions on a test in which there were 100 questions, his score would be 78 out of 100, or 78%. Percents are another way of indicating fractional part based on 100. They are extensively used in grading and banking systems.*

In order to change a fraction to a percent, you must first change the fraction to a decimal.

1.0 Changing Decimals to Percents

.62   .75   6.32   .07   .9

In order to change decimals to percents you must move the decimal point *two places* to the right and place a percent sign (%) at the end of your number. Moving the decimal in the line of decimals given above:

62%   75%   632%   7%   90%

When you *change a percent to a decimal,* you must reverse this procedure. Instead of moving to the right, you must move your decimal point two places to the left and place it there. For example: 22%, 22%, 22, .22

move two places   answer

39%	402%	55.5%	36.4%	20%
.39	4.02	.555	.364	.20

---

(1) Change these fractions to percents: round off to the nearest hundredth:

1.   a. $\dfrac{1}{2}$ b. $\dfrac{4}{5}$ c. $\dfrac{7}{10}$ d. $\dfrac{3}{7}$ e. $\dfrac{5}{8}$

2.   f. $\dfrac{3}{4}$ g. $2\dfrac{1}{6}$ h. $\dfrac{5}{2}$ i. $3\dfrac{1}{3}$ j. $\dfrac{9}{20}$

3.   k. $\dfrac{5}{13}$ l. $\dfrac{7}{18}$ m. $\dfrac{5}{16}$ n. $\dfrac{16}{3}$ o. $\dfrac{21}{4}$

4. In a 100 game season, the Tigers won 47 games. What percent of their games did they win? What percent of their games did they lose?

5. On a test of 50 questions, John got 7 wrong. What percent of the questions did he answer correctly? What percent did he answer incorrectly?

6. In a certain recipe, 3 parts of flour are added to 5 parts of cream. What percent of the mixture is cream? What percent of the mixture is flour? Round off to nearest thousandth.

7. In a baseball season, Phil got 37 hits in 100 times at bat. What percent of his times at bat were hits?

8. Charley scored an 85% on his grammar test. What fractional part of the test questions did he answer correctly? What fractional part did he answer wrong?

9. If a certain mixture is 46% alcohol, what fractional part is alcohol?

10. In Jamaica High School, 44% of the students attend morning session, 51% attend afternoon session, and 5% attend evening session. What fractional part of the total student body attends each of the three sessions?

11. If Peter invests 22% of his salary in bonds, what fractional part is he investing?

12. If 42 students in a group of 48 pass the equivalency test, what fractional part passed the test? What decimal part passed the test? What percent of the group passed the test?

2.0 Finding a Percent of a Number

Often, in the arithmetic of percents, you will be given a whole number and asked to find a percent of that whole number. To arrive at a correct answer you should use this formula:

MULTIPLY percent × whole = the part asked for. For example:

The Mets won 65% of their 100 games. How many games did they win?

$$65\% \times 100 \text{ games} = \text{part}$$

```
  100
×  .65
 -----
  500
  600
 -----
 65.00     Ans.  65 games won
```

Example: In a group of 350 students, 20% are in the advanced math class. How many students are in the advanced math class?

$$20\% \times 350 = \text{part}$$

```
  350
× .20
 -----
  000
  700
 -----
 70.00     Ans. 70 students in advanced math
```

> **Note 15.3**
> To perform arithmetic operations on percents, the percent must be changed into decimals or fractions.

---

(1) Find the percent part, when the percent and the whole are known of the following:

	(a)	(b)	(c)
1.	35% of 300	16% of 85	88% of 212
2.	72% of 65	525% of 50	68% of 112
3.	40% of 8	22% of 74	50% of 65
4.	175% of 12	41% of 90	152% of 60
5.	25.5% of 120	22½% of 70	58¼% of 150
6.	25% of $600	44% of $6.25	70% of $85.50
7.	30% of $50	45% of $5.75	70% of $90.30

8. 85% of 1300 students are going to college. What number are going to college?

9. William saves 45% of his $140 salary. How much money does he save?

10. A 12-ounce soft drink is 65% carbonated water. How much of the drink is carbonated water?

11. For the last 50 work days, Joan has been absent 4% of the time. How many days has she missed?

12. 62% of the city's 8,000,000 residents are Democrats. What number are Democrats?

13. 15% of Mr. Miller's class hours are spent in the lab. What part of his 280 work hours are spent in the lab?

14. 25% of the 540 students in the chemistry section are girls. How many girls are there in chemistry? How many boys?

15. 83% of the 12,000 people attending a meeting are school teachers. How many teachers attended the meeting?

16. In a group of 805, 48% voted to strike for more pay. How many voted to strike? How many did not vote to strike?

17. From a budget of $8,550, 25% is spent on books, 48% is spent on reading equipment, and 27% is spent on transportation. How much money is spent for each purpose?

18. 75% of $112,000 is allotted for worker's salaries. How much of the total is spent on salaries?

3.0 Finding a Whole, When Percent and a Certain Part Are Known

In order to find a greater whole, when a certain part is known, and the per cent of that certain part is also known, you must *divide the part by percent:*

$$\frac{part}{percent} = whole$$

Example: 15 is 60% of a total number. What is the number?

$$\frac{15}{.60} = whole \qquad .60./\overline{15.00}.$$

$$\begin{array}{r} 25. \\ 60/\overline{1500} \\ 120 \\ \hline 300 \\ 300 \\ \hline \end{array}$$

Ans. whole number = 25

Example: $72 is 75% of the money Rita takes home from work each week. What is the total money that she takes home?

$$\frac{72}{.75} = whole$$

$$\begin{array}{r} 96. \\ .75./\overline{72.00}. \\ 675 \\ \hline 450 \\ 450 \\ \hline \end{array}$$

Ans. $96 is Rita's take-home pay.

(1) Find the whole, when given part and percent in the following. Round off to the nearest hundredth.

	(a)	(b)	(c)
1.	15 is 6% of _____	44 is 10% of _____	38 is 5% of _____
2.	30 is 40% of _____	55 is 120% of _____	70 is 9% of _____
3.	100 is 12% of _____	50 is 50% of _____	30 is 8% of _____

4. 75 is 35.5% of _____   60 is 40.2% of _____   1,000 is 10% of _____

5. 9 is 200% of _____   80 is 16% of _____   5 is .8% of _____

6. Find the whole, when 12% of it is 65.

7. Find the whole, when 60% of it is 10.5.

8. Find the whole, when 75 is 20% of it.

9. Find the whole, when 45.8 is 5.5% of it.

10. The 40 games won in July and August represent 20% of the total games won. What is the total number of games won?

11. Franklin answered 18 questions correctly and received a grade of 90%. How many questions were there in all? How many did he answer incorrectly?

12. At a wholesale buying outfit, Mr. Graves paid $65.40 for a suit. This represented 60% of the total cost. What was the total cost of the suit?

13. 80% of a total enrollment is 2400. What is the total enrollment?

14. $45,000 represents 30% of the money given to a state program. What is the total amount given to the program?

15. Mr. Van Horn spends 42% of his grocery bill on meats. If he spends $13.50 a week on meats, what is his average weekly grocery bill?

16. The 120 stores of Ames Clothing that are in New York State represent 40% of the total amount of stores in the country. What is the total number of Ames Clothing Stores?

17. 5.7 feet is 85% of the height that Dolores will grow to. How tall will she be when she stops growing?

18. 145.4 tons is 90% of the weight of a week's farm produce at Valley Farms. What is the weight of the total week's produce?

19. $16.60 is 74% of Mrs. Jensen's personal expenses for a week. How much are her weekly personal expenses?

20. A man can do 80% of his week's work in 24 hours. How many hours will it take him to complete his week's work?

4.0 Finding What Percent One Number Is of Another

In some percent problems, you will be given the value of the part and the whole, and you will be asked to calculate the value of the percent. The rule is:

Divide, part ÷ whole = fraction, then fraction × 100 = percent

or $\dfrac{\text{part}}{\text{whole}}$ = fraction;

or whole$\overline{/\dfrac{\text{fraction as a decimal}}{\text{part}}}$;

then decimal × 100 = percent

Example: $18 is what part of $24?

$\dfrac{18}{24}$ = fraction;

fraction as a decimal:

```
        .75
  24/18.00
    168↓
    ─────
     120
     120
    ─────
```

percent:
.75 × 100 = 75%

Ans. $18 is 75% of $24.

Example: 62 tickets is what percent of the 460 tickets that were sold?

$\dfrac{62}{460}$

```
          .134
  460/62.000
     460↓|
     ─────
     1600 |
     1380↓
     ─────
     2200
```

Ans. .134 × 100 = 13.4%

(1) *Find what percent the part is of the whole of the following:*

(a)	(b)	(c)
1. 16 is ___% of 30	17 is ___% of 34	8 is ___% of 64
2. 20 is ___% of 100	40 is ___% of 60	100 is ___% of 50
3. 16 is ___% of 80	105 is ___% of 115	32 is ___% of 40
4. 510 is ___% of 200	85 is ___% of 115	72 is ___% of 88

5. What percent of 400 is 20?

6. What percent of 8,000 is 60?

7. What percent of 50.8 is 22.5?

8. What percent of 106.45 is 209.6?

9. What percent of $62.50 is $60?

10. What percent of 12 is 7.5?

11. $55 is what percent of a total bill of $90?

12. Charles spends $25 of his $125 pay on household items. What percent of his check is spent on household items?

13. A team wins 65 games and loses 45 games during a basketball season. What percent did they win? What percent of games played did they lose?

14. 5 weeks is what percent of a year?

15. 1 pint is what percent of a gallon?

16. 150 pounds is what percent of 1 ton?

17. 8 ounces is what percent of a quart?

18. Charles answered 35 questions right and 10 questions wrong. What percent of the total did he answer right? What percent did he answer wrong?

19. A television set that is listed to sell for $450 is reduced to $375. What is the percent of price reduction?

20. Mrs. Mathews buys a radio on sale for $78.50. The original price was $102. What percent of the original price did she pay?

21. A shirt that sells for $12 is reduced by $3 for a sale. What is the percent of reduction?

22. 300 out of 380 voters cast their votes for the Republican candidate. What percent of the voters voted Republican?

23. In 1971, a dealer sold 5,000 cars. In 1972, the dealer sold 7,500 cars. By what percent did his sales increase? What percent of his 1971 sales are his 1972 sales?

24. The price of chicken rose in the month of January from $.49 a pound to $.70 a pound. What was the percent of increase?

25. 34 players on a 36-man team reported no injuries after Saturday's game. What is the percent of players with injuries on the team?

26. 17 is what percent of 75?

27. 22 is what percent of 66?

28. 25 is what percent of 50?

29. 20 is what percent of 120?

30. 40 is what percent of 200?

31. 15 is what percent of 150?

32. 25 is what percent of 15?

33. 100 is what percent of 50?

34. .7 is what percent of .92?

35. 3.5 is what percent of 1.0?

36. 40 is 25% of what number?

37. 25 is 12.5% of what number?

38. 15 is 60% of what number?

39. 5 is 20% of what number?

40. 20 is 100% of what number?

41. 30 is 300% of what number?

42. 32% of a certain number is 80. What is the number?

SECTION VII
Verbal Problems -
Formula Problems

1.0 Areas of Common Geometric Figures

Observe the following figures.

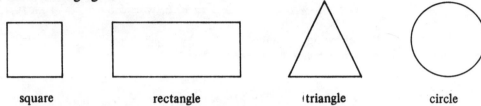

square   rectangle   ＋triangle   circle

These four geometric figures are the ones that will be covered on the High School Equivalency Test. You will be responsible for knowing the formulas that tell you the distance around the outer surface of each figure called and the area of space enclosed in each figure.

A.   THE RECTANGLE

The *rectangle* is a four-sided figure with two pairs of equal sides. The *longer side* of the rectangle is called *the length*. The *shorter side* of the rectangle is called *the width*. One long side equals the long side opposite it. One wide side equals the other wide side opposite it.

Examples of rectangles:

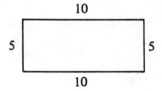   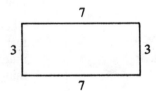   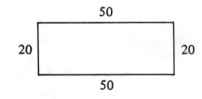

Perimeter—the distance around the outside border of any figure is the perimeter.

For a rectangle: Perimeter = length + length + width + width

or

P = 2 × length + 2 × width

Perimeter of rectangle = 2 l + 2 w

Area of a rectangle—the measurement of the space that is enclosed by the rectangle.

Area = length × width

A = l × w

67

(1) Find the perimeter of the following rectangles, when length and width are given.

(a)	(b)	(c)	(d)
1. l = 5, w = 3	l = 20, w = 6	l = 15, w = 12	l = 9, w = 8
2. l = 8, w = 5 1/2	l = 10, w = 3 1/4	l = 3 1/2, w = 3/4	l = 20, w = 7/2
3. l = 12, w = 5.5	l = 20, w = 13.8	l = 15.6, w = 5.8	l = 19.1, w = 10.9

(2) Find the area of the following rectangles, when length and width are given. Area is expressed as a *square measurement*.

(a)	(b)	(c)
1. l = 12, w = 8	l = 55, w = 20	l = 21, w = 16
2. l = 21 3/4, w = 15	l = 9 1/2, w = 6 2/3	l = 61 1/5, w = 25 1/2
3. l = 60.6, w = 40.4	l = 18.5, w = 9.8	l = 100.5, w = 10

(3) Find the length of the following rectangles, when width and area are given.

(a)	(b)	(c)
1. A = 100 sq. ft., w = 5 ft.	A = 600 sq. ft., w = 20 ft.	A = 48 sq. in., w = 6 in.
2. A = 186 sq. ft., w = 12 ft.	A = 164 2/3 sq. ft., w = 9 1/2 ft.	A = 425 2/5 sq. in., w = 19 1/2 ft.
3. A = 50.6 sq. ft., w = 5.5 ft.	A = 380.7 sq. ft., w = 16.2 ft.	A = 1536 sq. ft., w = 30 ft.

(4) Answer the following:

1. If a garden is 19 ft. 6 inches long and 15 ft. wide, how much fencing would be needed to surround the outside of this garden?

2. How many square feet of tile floor covering are needed to cover a floor 15.5 feet long and 13.3 feet wide?

3. What is the area of a football field that is 100 yds. long and 65 yds. wide?

4. If the area of a rectangular patch of fabric is 332 sq. inches, and the length of this fabric is 20 3/4 inches, then how wide is this patch of fabric?

5. The width of a swimming pool is 25.5 feet wide, and the length is twice as much. What is the area of this swimming pool?

B.   THE SQUARE

The *square* is a four-sided figure with all four equal sides. All sides of a square are equal.

Perimeter—the perimeter of a square is the sum of the four sides. You can tabulate the perimeter by multiplying the side by 4.

$$P = s + s + s + s \quad \text{or} \quad P = 4 \times s$$

(5) Find the perimeter of a square whose side is:

a) 5   b) 6 1/2   c) 5.8
d) 10.5   e) 30.3   f) 1
g) 17.2

(6) Find the area of a square that has a side of:

a) 16 1/2 in.   b) 5.8 ft.
c) 60.1 yards   d) 6.25 ft.
e) 5 1/3 ft.   f) 20 5/6 in.
g) 22.2 ft.   h) 6.6 in.
i) 15 2/5 in.   j) 20 3/5 ft.

(7) Answer the following:

1. What is the area of a baseball diamond that is 90 ft. on each side?

2. The area of a square plot of property is 3600 square yards. How much is the side of the square plot?

3. The foundation of a building is a square that is 60.4 ft. on each side. What is the perimeter of the foundation? What is the area of the foundation?

4. At a cost of $3 a square foot, how much money is paid for carpeting that is a square with a side of 15 ft.?

5. A square platform has a perimeter of 80 in. What is the area?

6. A square has a perimeter of 100 ft. What is its area?

C. THE TRIANGLE

The *triangle* is a three-sided figure which has base and height. The perimeter, once again, is the distance around the outside of the figure. Adding the three sides will give you the perimeter. The sides of a triangle can be equal or unequal.

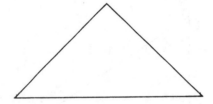

$$\textbf{Perimeter} = \text{side} + \text{side} + \text{side}$$

$$\textbf{Area} = \frac{\text{base} \times \text{height}}{2} \text{ or } \frac{1}{2} \, b \times h$$

The isosceles triangle is a triangle with two equal sides.

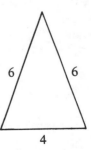

The equilateral triangle is a triangle with all sides equal.

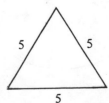

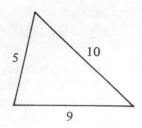

The scalene triangle is a triangle which has no equal sides.

(8) Find the area of the following triangles when given base and height. Use formula $1/2\ b \times h = A$

(a)	(b)	(c)	(d)
1. b = 5, h = 7	b = 10, h = 5	b = 16, h = 20	b = 4, h = 6
2. b = 16 1/2, h = 10	b = 10 1/3, h = 5	b = 12 3/4, h = 16	b = 9 1/2, h = 6
3. b = 20.5, h = 15.2	b = 12.6, h = 8.3	b = 14.4, h = 9.8	b = 3/4, h = 1 1/5

D.   THE RIGHT TRIANGLE

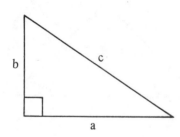

A right triangle is a triangle with a right angle, which is an angle of 90°. Right triangles will be called such, to separate them from other triangles. A right triangle has two legs and a *hypotenuse*. In a right triangle the hypotenuse is the longest side and is opposite the right angle. In the diagram to the left, the legs are labelled a and b. The hypotenuse is labelled c. In all right triangles, the square of one leg plus the square of the other will add to the square of the hypotenuse. This is the Pythagorean theorem.

E.   THE CIRCLE

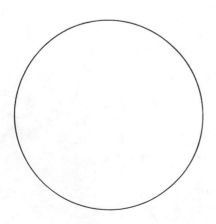

The circle is a round geometric figure formed by a revolution of an equal radius from the center of the circle. Every circle has a *diameter, radii,* and a *circumference.*

Circles, like other geometric figures, have area. *The diameter* is a line which passes through the center of the circle and cuts the circle into two equal halves or semicircles.

The circumference represents the distance around the outside arc of the circle. Circumference and perimeter of a circle mean the same thing.

The radius is a straight line connecting the center of the circle with any point on the outside edge.

The symbol π is a Greek letter, read as "pi," that represents the approximate sum of 22/7 or in decimals, 3.14. The formula for the circumference of a circle is:

Circumference $= 2\,\pi\,r$;   ($2 \times \pi \times r$,   when   r stands for radius)

Example: If the radius of a given circle $= 21$, then the circumference would be:

$$C = 2 \times \frac{22}{7} \times 21 \qquad C = 2 \times \frac{\overset{3}{22}}{\underset{1}{7}} \times 21$$

$$C = 2 \times 66$$
$$C = 132$$

The diameter of a circle is twice the size of the radius.

$$D = 2r$$

(9) Use the given information to determine the circumferences of the following circles (use $\pi = \frac{22}{7}$)

1. radius of the circle $= 49$ C $=$ _____
2. radius of the circle $= 28$ C $=$ _____
3. radius of the circle $= 70$ C $=$ _____
4. diameter of the circle $= 14$ C $=$ _____
5. radius of the circle $= 10$ C $=$ _____
6. diameter of the circle $= 8$ C $=$ _____
7. diameter of the circle $= 15$ C $=$ _____
8. radius of the circle $= 20$ C $=$ _____
9. radius of the circle $= 31\ 1/2$ C $=$ _
10. radius of the circle $= 9$ C $=$ _____

The area of the circle is the measurement of all the space enclosed by that circle and the formula for area of a circle is:

Area $= \pi \times$ radius^2
$A = \pi\,r^2$

Sample problem

Find the area of a circle with a radius of 10.

$$3.14 \times 10^2 = 3.14 \times 100 = 314$$

(10) Find the areas of the following circles (use $\pi = 3.14$):

1. radius $= 12$ area $=$ _____?
2. radius $= 4$ area $=$ _____?
3. radius $= 100$ area $=$ _____?
4. radius $= 5$ area $=$ _____?
5. diameter $= 30$ area $=$ _____?
6. diameter $= 50$ area $=$ _____?
7. diameter $= 12.8$ area $=$ _____?
8. radius $= 8.8$ area $=$ _____?
9. radius $= 6.1$ area $=$ _____?
10. radius $= 5.2$ area $=$ _____?

2.0 Pythagorean Theorem

$$a^2 + b^2 = c^2$$

By computing the square root of c^2, one can find the hypotenuse when the legs are known. By computing the square roots of a^2 or b^2, one can find either leg, when one leg and the hypotenuse are known. The hypotenuse is longer than either leg.

Sample problem

If a right triangle has a leg of 3 ft., and a second leg of 4 ft., what is the hypotenuse?

$$a^2 + b^2 = c^2$$
$$3^2 + 4^2 = c^2 \quad 9 + 16 = c^2 \quad 25 = c^2 \quad 5 = c$$

(11) Find the hypotenuse, when both legs are given in the following examples:

1. leg $a = 15$, leg $b = 20$, hypotenuse = _____

2. leg $a = 21$, leg $b = 28$, hypotenuse = _____

3. leg $a = 6$, leg $b = 8$, hypotenuse = _____

4. leg $a = 12$, leg $b = 16$, hypotenuse = _____

5. leg $a = 9$, leg $b = 12$, hypotenuse =

(12) Find the base of the following triangles, when height and area are given:

1. Area = 50, height = 20, base = __

2. Area = 20, height = 8, base = _____

3. Area = 26, height = 4, base = _____

4. Area = 7, height = 14, base = _____

5. Area = 6, height = 24, base = _____

3.0 Summary of Formulas for Area and Perimeter

Rectangle—	perimeter	—$P = 2l + 2w$
	area	—$A = l \times w$
Square—	perimeter	—$P = 4s$
	area	—$A = s^2$
Triangle—	perimeter	—$P =$ sum of three sides
	area	—$A = 1/2\ bh$ or $\dfrac{bh}{2}$
Circle—	Circumference	—$C = 2\pi r$
	Area	—$A = \pi r^2$

4.0 Reading Formulas

Mathematics can be compared to a language. As in a language, mathematics uses symbols to stand for ideas, concepts, or quantities. Also, it uses these symbols to express relationships between quantities. These relationships are called formulas.

Example:
$$D = \text{Distance}$$
$$R = \text{Rate}$$
$$T = \text{Time}$$

then $$D = RT$$

In this example, the symbols used are D, R, and T and they stand for the quantities Distance, Rate, and Time. Their relationship is given by the formula $D = RT$. If we were to translate this into an equivalent English statement it would read, "Distance is equal to the product of the quantities rate and time."

In this section are exercises to help you develop the skill of reading mathematical formulas.

Look at the figure below, then answer the questions that follow.

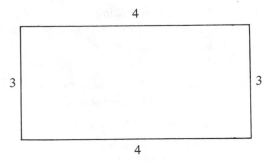

(13) Questions:

1. This figure is a rectangle.
    True _____ False _____

2. The lengths of the opposite sides of the rectangle are (3,3) and (4,4).
    True _____ False _____

3. We can say that the opposite sides of a rectangle are always equal.
    True _____ False _____

If the shorter side is called the width, and is represented by the symbol (w), and the longer side is called the length and is represented by the symbol (l), identify the formula that corresponds to the following statements.

4. The perimeter (P), of a rectangle is equal to twice its width plus twice its length.
    a) $P = 2w + 1$
    b) $P = w + 2l$
    c) $P = 2w + 2l$
    Ans: _____

5. The area (A) of a rectangle is equal to the product of its width and length.
    a) $A = w + 1$
    b) $A = wl$
    c) $A = w - 1$
    d) $A = w/l$
    Ans: _____

Given: *A square is a rectangle whose sides have all the same length.*

Identify the square

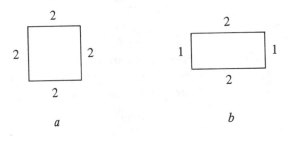

a   *b*

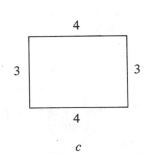

c

Answer = *a*

(14) Identify the correct formula for the following statements.

1. The perimeter (P) of a square whose side is represented by the letter "s" is four times its side.
   a) $P = 4s$
   b) $P = 4s + 1$
   c) $P = s + s$

   Ans. _____

2. The area of a square is its side multiplied by itself.
   a) $A = s$
   b) $A = 2s$
   c) $A = s \times s$

   Ans. _____

3. If
   A_R = Area of a Rectangle
   P_R = Perimeter of a Rectangle
   A_S = Area of a Square
   P_S = Perimeter of a Square

Identify the following equations by inserting the proper symbol in the space provided.

1) _____ $= s \cdot s$
2) _____ $= 2l + 2w$
3) _____ $= 4s$
4) _____ $= l \cdot w$

4. If
   "I" represents interest
   "P" represents principal
   "R" represents rate per year
   "T" represents time

   Given the formula
   $$I = PRT$$

   Complete the following statement by inserting the correct word in the space provided.

   Interest is equal to the product of the _____, the _____, and the _____.

5. If "D" represents distance traveled
   "R" represents the rate of movement
   "T" represents time

Given: $D = RT$
Complete the following:
   Distance equals the _____ of rate and _____.

6. Given: $R = D / T$

   Complete the following:
   Rate equals the _____ divided by the _____.

7. If
   "A" represents the area of a triangle
   "b" represents the base of a triangle
   "h" represents the altitude of a triangle

   Given: $A = 1/2\ bh$

   Complete the following:
   The area of a triangle is _____ the product of the _____ and _____.

8. If
   "A" represents the area of a circle
   "r" represents the radius of a circle
   "π" is a constant equal to 3.14 (called pi)

   Given: $A = \pi r^2$

   Complete the following:
   The area of a circle is equal to the _____ of _____ and the _____ squared.

9. Given: $C = 2\pi r$, where "C" represents the circumference of a circle.

   Complete the following:
   The circumference of a circle is equal to twice the _____ of _____ and the _____.

10. If
    "V" represents the volume of a cube
    "l" represents the length of a cube
    "h" represents the height of a cube
    "d" represents the depth of a cube

Given: $V = lhd$

Complete the following:

The _____ of a cube is equal to the _____ of the _____ _____, the _____, and the _____.

You are now ready to develop your own formulas or equations. Look at the example below.

If **P** represents the number of patients a doctor normally sees in one day, write the mathematical expressions for the following statements.

a) Monday he saw *twice as many* patients. _____ (2P)

b) Tuesday he saw *five less* than normal. _____ (P − 5)

c) Wednesday he saw *ten more* patients than normal. _____ (P + 10)

d) Thursday he saw *one half as many* patients. _____ (1/2 P)

(15) Questions:
1. In the statements above, the italicized phrases contain the key words.

True _____ False _____

2. They are called key words because they establish relationships between the number of patients the doctor saw on a given day, and the number of patients he normally sees.

True _____ False _____

3. These key words are represented mathematically as follows:
"twice as many" . . . 2
"five less" . . . −5

"ten more" . . . + 10
"one half as many" . . . 1/2

True _____ False _____

Now do the following exercises.

(16) For each of the following statements write the mathematical expressions in the space provided.

1. 12 divided by some number (x) is equal to 3. _____ = _____.

2. 12 divided by some number (x) is equal to three times some other number (y). _____ = _____.

3. 12 minus 3 equals three times some number x. _____ = _____.

4. A number (x) divided by two times another number (y) equals 5. _____ _____ = _____.

5. The difference between 16 and some number (x), divided by 2 equals 6. _____ = _____.

6. Some number (x) minus 9 is equal to five times the number. _____ = _____.

7. 5 plus 3 is equal to two times some other number (x). _____ = _____.

8. Some number (x) divided by 5, plus 3 equals to two times another number y. _____ = _____.

You should now be aware that every statement has one or more thought units and that these thought units can be put into a mathematical expression.

Look at the statement below. It is the same as the preceding statement 5. Try to see how each thought for the complete unit is translated into its mathematical equivalent.

(Statement 5) The difference between 16 and some number (x), divided by 2, equals 6.

Thought-Unit   *Mathematical Equivalent*

The difference between 16 $16 - x$
and some number (x).

divided by 2 $/2$

equals 6 $= 6$

Putting it all together, we have

(Difference between 16 and some number)→$\dfrac{16 - x}{2}$ $= 6 \leftarrow$(six)
                                                        ↑__(equals)
                                                   __(Divided by 2)

amount he borrowed, how much did
he borrow? _____ = _____.

---

(17) In the following exercise let the letter (x)
      represent the unknown number or quan-
      tity. Write the mathematical expression for
      the following statements.

      Example:
      If the ages of two men differ by five, and
      if the older of the two is forty years old,
      how old is the younger man?
      Let x = unknown quantity i.e. the age of
      the younger man, then $x = 40 - 5$.
      This is read as follows: the age of the
      younger man is five less than the age of the
      older man.

   1. If a telephone pole is 3 times as tall
      as a 10 ft. lamp post, write the expres-
      sion for how tall the pole is. _____
      = _____.

   2. If a person has $20 and each day he
      spends $3.00, write expression for
      how much will he have left after three
      days. _____ = _____.

   3. John had seven books. He bought
      more and now has 16. What is the
      expression for how many more books
      he bought? _____ = _____.

   4. The sum of two numbers is 21. If the
      larger number is twice the smaller
      number, what is the value of the
      smaller number? _____ = _____.

   5. If a person borrowed some money and
      paid back $25.00 which is half of the

(18) Match each mathematical expression be-
      low with its equivalent written statement,
      by inserting the letter of the mathematical
      expression next to its equivalent statement.

      a) $x + 9 = 20$ e) $x = \dfrac{30 - 14}{2}$
      b) $x - 9 = 20$ f) $x = 30 - 14$
      c) $2(x + 9) = 20$ g) $2x = 30 - 14$
      d) $x - 9/2 = 20$ h) $x = 30 + 14$

   1. What number is the difference be-
      tween 30 and 14? _____

   2. The difference of some number and
      9 equals 4 times 5. _____

   3. One half the difference of some num-
      ber and 9 equals 20. _____

   4. 2 times the sum of some numbers
      and 9 equals 20. _____

   5. There are 30 students in a class. On
      Monday 14 were absent, how many
      were present? _____

   6. 44 is the answer to which statement?
      _____

   7. The sum of some number and 9 is
      equal to twice 10. _____

   8. Some number is equal to half the dif-
      ference of 30 and 14. _____

   9. Twice some number equals the dif-
      ference of 30 and 14. _____

  10. One half the difference of 30 and 14
      equals some number. _____

SECTION VIII
Bases and Exponents and Literal Notation

1.0 Bases and Exponents

10^2 The number to the left is called *10 squared* or *ten to the second power*.

The base number is 10.

The exponent is the smaller number above the base. In this case the exponent is 2.

Note 16

In order to find 10 to the second power, you must multiply 10×10. All numbers to the second power are found by multiplying the base number times itself. When the exponent is 2, simply copy the base number two times and multiply.

Examples:

$6^2 = 6 \times 6$ $7^2 = 7 \times 7$

$\left(\dfrac{1}{4}\right)^2 = \dfrac{1}{4} \times \dfrac{1}{4}$ $.5^2 = .5 \times .5$

$20^2 = 20 \times 20$ $50^2 = 50 \times 50$

Note 17

10^3 A base with an exponent of 3 is called a number to *the third power* or a *number cubed*. Multiply base $\times$ base $\times$ base. Copy the base down three times and multiply.

$10^3 = 10 \times 10 \times 10 = 1,000$
$5^3 = 5 \times 5 \times 5 = 125$

Note 18

The power of a number tells us *how many times* the base number is multiplied.

---

(1) What do these numbers express?

a. 6^3 b. 7^2 c. 4^4 d. 5^6 e. 7^4 f. 2^5 g. 3^4

(2) Express these numbers as powers of the base:

a. 7×7
b. $6 \times 6 \times 6 \times 6$
c. $5 \times 5 \times 5$
d. $1 \times 1 \times 1 \times 1$
e. $10 \times 10 \times 10$
f. $2 \times 2 \times 2 \times 2 \times 2 \times 2$
g. 20×20
h. $50 \times 50 \times 50 \times 50$
i. $9 \times 9 \times 9 \times 9 \times 9 \times 9$

Note 19

All numbers with the exponent 1 are expressed as numbers to the power of one, or to the first power. Any base to the exponent one is equal to the base. For example:

$6^1 = 6,$ $100^1 = 100,$

$1,000,000^1 = 1,000,000,$ $\left(\dfrac{1}{2}\right)^1 = \dfrac{1}{2}$

Note 20

In general when a number is given as
$$N = \text{number}$$
and when this number is raised to a specific power (P) then we speak of the number as the *base* and the *power* as the exponent. We write N^P, which means N is the *base* and P is the exponent or *power*.

Note 21

All numbers or bases to the exponent 0 are bases to the zero power. All bases to the zero power are equal to 1.

$6^0 = 1$ $10^0 = 1$ $5^0 = 1$

$1,000^0 = 1$ $.3^0 = 1$ $\left(\dfrac{1}{2}\right)^0 = 1$

---

(3) Evaluate the following bases to their exponents:

a. $7^2 =$ d. $10^3 =$ g. $7^3 =$ j. $100^2 =$
b. $6^3 =$ e. $10^1 =$ h. $20^2 =$ k. $5^4 =$
c. $2^5 =$ f. $9^0 =$ i. $40^2 =$ l. $4^4 =$

m. express 36 as a power of 2
n. express 8 as a power of 3
o. express 10,000 as a power of 10
p. express 125 as a power of 5
q. express 64 as a power of 4
r. express 64 as a power of 2

(4) Find the following numbers:

1. 5×10^3 2. 6×5^4 3. 7×10^0 4. 8×8^2
5. 10×3^3 6. 3.5×10^2 7. 4.1×6^2 8. 10.3×2^4
9. 5.5×5^3 10. 20.5×2^2 11. 5×4^5 12. 20×10^1

2.0 Literal Notation

When we discuss geometric areas and algebra problems, we will use letters to represent terms which may be known or unknown. For example:

Length $\times$ width $= 1 \times w$. Here the letters 1 and w represent the unknown length and width. Because of the nature of algebra, you will eliminate the ($\times$) multiplication sign. You will use no sign between two letters to show multiplication. For example:

$$1 \times w = lw \qquad k \times t = kt \qquad 2 \times w = 2w$$
$$a \times b = ab \qquad r \times t = rt \qquad 5 \times 1 = 5l$$

For any other operation in *literal mathematics,* you will use the ($-$) ($+$) ($\div$) signs. A fraction line also means division. For example:

$$\frac{a}{b} = a \div b \qquad\qquad \frac{a}{2} = a \div 2$$

$$\frac{r}{t} = r \div t \qquad\qquad \frac{lw}{2} = lw \div 2$$

(5) Using letters and signs, represent the following mathematical operations:

a. a plus b
b. c decreased by d
c. 2 times h
d. the product of a, b, and c
e. a divided by 3
f. the product of a and b and divided by 3
g. h increased by 5
h. 5 diminished by a
i. k to the fifth power
j. the sum of a, b, and d
k. the difference between c and b
l. the quotient of b and a
m. 2 times the sum of x and y
n. 1/2 as much as the product of b and h

You will learn more literal notation in the Algebra section.

SECTION IX
Algebra

In algebra, you will be using symbols to represent quantities. Letters will be substituted for numbers. Algebra uses a system of literal notation. In algebra problems, you will use the known information to solve for the unknown quantity. Note the unknown quantity X as it goes through the arithmetic operations.

ADDITION

2 added to X
2 plus X
X increased by 2
X and 2
The sum of X and 2

$= X + 2$

SUBTRACTION

The difference between X and 2
X less 2
X diminished by 2
X decreased by 2
X minus 2

$= X - 2$

MULTIPLICATION

The product of 2 and X
2 times X
twice X
2 times as great as X

$= 2X$

NOTE: Remember *NOT* to use the multiplication sign with algebra. *NO SIGN* between two factors indicates multiplication.

DIVISION

X divided by 2
X ÷ 2

How many 2's in X?

$\frac{1}{2} X$

$= \dfrac{X}{2}$, or $X \div 2$

(1) Do the following problems as per the sample 1:

Example:

1. John has n pairs of pants. Represent the addition of 3 more pairs.

   Ans. n + 3

2. Peter travelled X miles. Represent the distance he travels when he goes 3 times as far.

3. Janice is y years old. Represent her age 3 years ago. Represent her age 5 years from now in the future.

4. Mr. Peters has made X money from his sales commissions. Represent his money divided among his two partners and himself.

5. Represent the number of inches in Z feet. Represent the number of feet in K inches.

6. Roberta is C years old. Her sister, Connie, is twice as old as Roberta. Represent Connie's age.

7. Harold is d inches tall. Represent his height now that he has grown 4 inches taller.

8. Mrs. Royce has a dollars. Mrs. Simpson has b dollars. Represent the amount of dollars they have together.

9. A jeweler has d amount of bracelets. Represent the amount of bracelets he has once he has sold 6.

10. Represent the number of quarts in X gallons.

11. A school has a amount of students in attendance. Half of these students attend an evening session. Represent the amount of students that attend the evening session.

12. Rita has X amount of dimes. She has 3 times as many nickels as dimes, and 1/4 as many quarters as dimes. Represent the amount of quarters and nickels that she has.

1.0 Combining Literal Terms

A. *Coefficients*—The number that often precedes the algebra letter term is called the coefficient. If the literal number x has a coefficient of 5, it will appear as 5x. If the literal number y has a coefficient of 1/2, it will appear as $\frac{1}{2}$ y.

Examples:

(A) 5x = 5 times y

(B) $\frac{1}{2}$ y = 1/2 of y

When you begin to solve algebra equations, you will determine a number that equals a letter. If, in example (A), you should determine x to be 3, then the value of 5x would be 5 times 3 or 15.
If, in example (B), you should determine y to be 10, then the value of $\frac{1}{2}$y would be 1/2 of 10, or 5.

(2) In the following examples, combine the coefficients when your literal terms are alike. Notice the sample problems.

(A) 2x + 5x + x = 8x

Do not combine terms which have unlike letters, as shown in sample (B).

(B) 2x + 3y + x + 2y = 3x + 5y

1. 3x + 5x + 4x = _____

2. 5a + 3a + a = _____

3. $\frac{1}{6}$y + $\frac{3}{6}$y + $\frac{1}{6}$y = _____

4. .5a + 1.6a + 3.4a = _____

5. 5y − 3y = _____

6. 3.8b − 1.62b = _____

7. 7c − 6c = _____

8. 4.2z − 2.0z = _____

9. 3h + a + 5h + 3a = _____

10. 17x + y + 4x + 6y = _____

11. 17x + 5y − 3x − 2y = _____

12. 6d + 4y − 2d = _____

13. (5e + 2e) − 6e = _____

14. 6y + (3y − y) = _____

15. 6x + 2a − 3x + 5a + 3y = _____

16. 5b + 3a + 5h − 4b − a − 2h = _____

B. *Evaluation of Algebra terms*—When you *evaluate* algebraic expressions, you will be given the value for the unknowns. Once you know the values of the unknown terms, you must substitute this value for the letters. Notice the model problems:

(A) When a = 3 and b = 2 *evaluate:* $\frac{6b}{a}$

answer

$$\frac{6b}{a} = \frac{6 \times 2}{3} = \frac{12}{3} = 4$$

(B) When x = 4 and y = $\frac{1}{2}$ *evaluate:* 5xy

answer

$$5xy = 5 \times 4 \times \frac{1}{2} = 20 \times \frac{1}{2} = 10$$

(C) When c = 3, d = 10, y = 5 *evaluate:* (3c + 2d) − 5y

answer

$$(3c + 2d) − 5y = (9 + 20) − 25 =$$
$$29 − 25 = 4$$

(3) Evaluate the following expressions when x = 2 and y = 10:

1. $2xy = $ _____

2. $2x + 2y = $ _____

3. $2y - 5x = $ _____

4. $4x + 2y = $ _____

5. $\dfrac{xy}{2} = $ _____

6. $100xy$ _____

7. $(5y - 7) + 3x = $ _____

8. $\dfrac{3xy}{15} = $ _____

9. $.5xy + 4.7 = $ _____

10. $\dfrac{6y}{3x} + \dfrac{x}{y} = $ _____

2.0 Negative Numbers

At this point, it is important that you learn negative numbers. Negative numbers are those numbers on the number line that are less than zero. They proceed to negative infinity just as positive numbers proceed to positive infinity. This is illustrated by the following:

Positive and negative whole integers

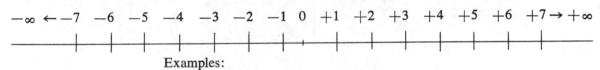

Examples:

(A) If the temperature on a given day is 15 degrees, and by nightfall, it drops 20 more degrees, then the new temperature is recorded as 5 degrees below, or −5.

This can be shown by the number line as:

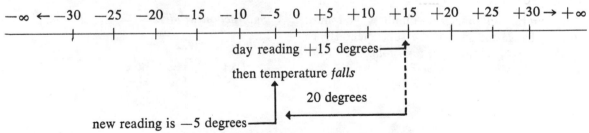

day reading +15 degrees

then temperature *falls*

20 degrees

new reading is −5 degrees

(B) If an individual owes $200 and possesses $125 then his financial holdings are −$75.

You can add, subtract, multiply, and divide negative numbers just as you did with positive numbers. There are certain rules that you must learn for each arithmetic operation dealing with negative numbers.

3.0 Procedure for Arithmetic of Negative Numbers

Addition of negative numbers

Negative numbers are recognized by their minus signs. Positive numbers will have either a plus sign or no sign. We call the number line of all numbers *signed numbers*. In the addition of signed numbers there are two rules to follow:

Note 22

If the signs of your addition numbers are the same, then add your numbers and keep the same sign.

Note 23

If the signs of your numbers which are being added are different, then you must find the new number by carrying out the operation as per example (B) and keep the sign of the larger signed number.

Examples:

(A) If signs are the same in addition, then add and keep the sign

$$
\begin{array}{cccccc}
+5 & 3 & -7 & -9 & -8 & +9 \\
+7 & 6 & -4 & -6 & 0 & 5 \\
\hline
12 & 9 & -11 & -15 & -8 & 14
\end{array}
$$

(B) If signs are different in addition, subtract smaller number from larger number and keep the sign of the number which is further than the other number from zero on the number line.

Add:
$$
\begin{array}{cccccc}
-7 & +8 & 5 & -10 & 6 & -7 \\
2 & -6 & -4 & 5 & -11 & +9 \\
\hline
-5 & 2 & 1 & -5 & -5 & 2
\end{array}
$$

(4) Add these signed numbers:

	(a)	(b)	(c)	(d)	(e)
1.	-5	0	-7	14	6
	-7	$+8$	-7	-3	-9

	(a)	(b)	(c)	(d)	(e)
2.	11	-5	$+7$	-9	10
	-3	5	2	-5	-6

3.	-103	$+180$	18	-33	-21
	-26	-640	-25	-330	20

4.0 Subtraction of Signed Numbers

In subtraction of signed numbers you must *always* change the sign of the subtrahend. Once you have changed the sign, *then follow the rules for addition of signed numbers.*

Example:

number
subtrahend
———————
difference   number − subtrahend = difference

(note to change the sign of the subtrahend regardless of whether its *original* sign was *plus* or *minus*)

Subtraction Models

Subtract:

(A)
$$
\begin{array}{ll}
5 & \text{note} \\
-4 & \text{sign} \\
\hline
 & \text{change} \rightarrow
\end{array}
\qquad
\begin{array}{l}
5 \\
+4 \\
\hline
9
\end{array}
$$

(B)
$$
\begin{array}{ll}
-17 & \text{note} \\
22 & \text{sign} \\
\hline
 & \text{change} \rightarrow
\end{array}
\qquad
\begin{array}{l}
-17 \\
-22 \\
\hline
-39
\end{array}
$$

(C)
$$
\begin{array}{ll}
+50 & \text{note} \\
+33 & \text{sign} \\
\hline
 & \text{change} \rightarrow
\end{array}
\qquad
\begin{array}{l}
+50 \\
-33 \\
\hline
+17
\end{array}
$$

(5) Subtract the following signed numbers. (Note to always change the sign of the subtrahend.)

	(a)	(b)	(c)	(d)	(e)
1.	−5	+17	161	23	171
	−4	+14	−80	−23	+18
2.	−300	55.2	168.51	+81.5	−70
	−200	+33.7	−33.22	+40.2	−70
3.	16 1/2	+12 3/4	+90	−60	+8 1/2
	8 1/4	+5 1/2	+100	−75 1/3	+ 7/8

5.0 Multiplication of Signed Numbers

When you multiply signed numbers, you must examine the signs of each of your numbers. If both of your numbers have the same sign, then your answer is positive. If both of your numbers have different signs, then your answer is negative. Or stating this another way a (−) times a (+) number always gives a (−) number.

Multiplication Models

Multiply:

	(A)	(B)	(C)	(D)
	−5	60	70.1	10.5
	−5	−3	−2.2	−2
	+25	−180	1402	−21.0
			1402	
			−154.22	

Note 24

When you are multiplying more than three numbers, your answer is *positive* if you have an even number of negative signs (if the actual number count of negative signs is 2, 4, 6, 8, etc.). Your answer is negative if the number of negatively signed numbers is odd. Notice the examples below:

(A) You have 2 negative numbers, which is an even number of negative numbers. Your answer is positive.

(−8) times (2) times (−3) = 48

(B) You only have 1, an odd number, negative sign. Therefore your answer must be negative.

(−5) times (3) times (5) = −75

(6) Multiply the following signed numbers:

	(a)	(b)	(c)	(d)	(e)
1.	−6	15	−30	−10.5	+60
	−8	−3	−10	100	+2
2.	7.5	6 1/2	−20	8	19
	−3.2	−2 1/4	−10	5	2

3.
$-2\,1/2$	$8\,1/5$	-8	20	30
$-3\,1/3$	-3	-5	-1	-3
		2		-5
				-1

6. $(-1/2)\,(1/4)\,(1/3) = $ _____

7. $(-13.1)\,(+2)\,(+5)\,(+1) = $ ____

8. $(-5)\,(-6)\,(-7) = $ _____

9. $(-12)\,(-2)\,(-3)\,(+1) = $ ____

4. $(-5)\,(8)\,(9) = $ _____

5. $(6.1)\,(4.2)\,(-5)\,(-2) = $ _____

10. $(-5)\,(-5)^2 = $ _____

6.0 Division of Signed Numbers

When you are dividing signed numbers you have two numbers — a divisor and a dividend. If the signs of these numbers are *the same*, then the answer will always be positive. If the signs of your divisor and dividend are different, then your answer will always be negative.

Division Models

(A)

$$-6 \div -3 = +2$$

(B)

$$-10 \overline{/50} \quad \overset{-5}{}$$

(C)

$$\frac{+24}{+3} = +8$$

(7) Divide the following signed numbers:

(a)   (b)   (c)   (d)   (e)

1. $\dfrac{-16}{4} = ?$ $\dfrac{-20}{-5} = ?$ $\dfrac{100}{+10} = ?$ $\dfrac{60}{-15} = ?$ $\dfrac{22}{-5} = ?$

2. $44 \div 4$ $62 \div -6$ $\dfrac{-7}{2} \div \dfrac{5}{4}$ $-16 \div 2.4$ $+88 \div -8$

3. $-9\overline{/6.03}$ $-7\overline{/49.77}$ $+6.2\overline{/-.310}$ $17\overline{/340}$ $12\overline{/-144}$

7.0 Evaluation of Signed Number Terms

Just as you evaluated algebra terms when positive numbers were used, you can also evaluate algebra terms with signed numbers.

On the G.E.D.T. you will be given literal equations and you will substitute number values for letter expressions.

(8) Evaluate the following algebraic expressions. Here are your number values:

$$x = 2 \qquad y = 3 \qquad z = 4$$

1. y^2 　　　 2. $x^2 y^2$ 　　　 3. $\dfrac{x^2 y}{z}$ 　　　 4. $3x^2$ 　　　 5. $(3x)^2$

6. $\dfrac{yz}{x}$ 　　　 7. $\dfrac{z^2}{x}$ 　　　 8. $5x + 2y$ 　　　 9. $3x + 4z$ 　　　 10. $x + y + z$

11. $3z - 2x$ 　　　 12. $y^2 - 2z$ 　　　 13. $4x \quad z$ 　　　 14. $\dfrac{z \mid y}{x}$ 　　　 15. $-2x + -3y$

16. $-5x^2$ 　　　 17. $(-5x)^2$ 　　　 18. z^3 　　　 19. x^5 　　　 20. $\dfrac{3xy + 4z}{x}$

8.0 Solving Algebraic Equations

We have reached the point where you can work with algebraic equations and not just algebraic expressions. In order to solve algebraic equations, you must use mathematical operations to determine a number value for the literal expression. You are going to solve for the unknown term in your equation by finding a known number value for this unknown term.

Solving for x, unknown term

X is the most common used literal number. It stands for a quantity which is now unknown, but will later be known. When x is determined to be a certain positive or negative value, it then becomes a known term.

If you were to be told that a person had a certain amount of money in his pocket which is called x dollars, you would have no idea of the known value of the sum of money. However, if you were told that "adding 5 to this unknown quantity would give me $25.," then you could deduce the amount of money that was held. You would calculate that the unknown amount (x) is such that when 5 is added to it, the amount becomes 25. Now writing this in a literal equation:

$$x + 5 = 25$$

This is the equation you would use to solve this particular problem.

In order to solve equations in algebra, you must determine the value for the unknown literal term. When you are given an algebraic equation, you may subtract, add, multiply, or divide *each side* of the equal sign by the same number without changing the value of the equation. By adding, subtracting, multiplying, or dividing you can isolate all of your unknown terms on one side of the equation and all of your number terms, positive or negative, on the other side of the equation. Notice these sample problems:

(A) $x + 2 = 9$
(B) $x - 5 = 7$
(C) $2x = 20$
(D) $\dfrac{x}{2} = 9$

In each of these equations, it is possible to arrive at a solution by just thinking about the equation.

For example:

A. $x + 2 = 9$

This equation states that some unknown value, when increased by 2 will give you nine. Now, what number, when added to two will give you nine? You would answer 7, and x does equal 7. Here is the way that you would solve the equation:

$x + 2 = 9$ ① Now, you must get the known numbers on one side and the unknown numbers on the other side.

$$x + 2 = 9$$
$$\underline{-2 \quad -2}$$

② By subtracting 2 from each side, you can leave x on the left side by itself. The last step in any algebra solution is the isolating of a single unknown term on one side of the equation.

$$\begin{array}{r} x + 2 = 9 \\ \underline{-2 \quad -2} \\ x \qquad = 7 \end{array}$$

③ 2 and −2 will cancel each other out. The x is then carried down, and in order to remain true to mathematical laws, you must subtract 2 from the 9 side also.

$x = 7$ ④ Notice that you are left with the equation $x = 7$.

Under the same principle of subtraction from each side, try these examples.

(9) Work for a solution for x.

(a)	(b)	(c)	(d)
1. $x + 5 = 9$	$x + 1 = 6$	$x + 4 = 9$	$x + 30 = 60$
2. $10 = x + 1$	$16 = x + 15$	$20 = x + 8$	$100 = x + 46$

B. Solving for x. Now consider this example:

$x - 5 = 7$ ① In examples of algebra that follow this pattern, you must add a number to both sides of the equation in order to solve for x. Notice that you have an unknown and a known term on the left side and a known term on the right side.

$$\begin{array}{l} x - 5\ (+5) = 7\ (+5) \\ x - 5 + 5 = 7 + 5 \\ x = 7 + 5 \end{array}$$

② You must bring the known term on the left over to the right side. What must you add to −5 in order to cancel it from the left side? Your answer should be +5.

$x = 12$ ③ By adding 5 to each side of the equation, you arrive at the answer $x = 12$.

(10) Solve the following examples of this type. You will need to add a quantity to both sides of the equation.

(a)	(b)	(c)	(d)
1. $x - 9 = 12$	$x - 10 = 30$	$x - 4 = 6$	$x - 7 = 12$

2. $x - 6 = 7$ $x - 7 = 0$ $x - 5 = 8$ $x - 3 = 12$

3. $15 = x - 5$ $22 = x - 8$ $-60 = x + 20$ $-15 = x + 20$

C. Solving for x, reduction of unknown term coefficient. This example is just a little bit different from A and B:

$2x = 20$

① In some algebra equations, you must reduce the number of x's that you have so that you have but one single x equaling one known quantity.

② In these examples, you divide the x term by its coefficient and then divide the known quantity by this same coefficient number as shown:

$$\frac{2x}{2} = \frac{20}{2}$$

③ Divide both sides by 2

$x = 10$

④ The answer is $x = 10$

(11) Solve the following equations by reducing the unknown to one unknown term:

	(a)	(b)	(c)	(d)
1.	$3x = 30$	$15x = 60$	$7x = 49$	$5x = 55$
2.	$6x = 60$	$8x = 160$	$4x = 16$	$-4x = 20$
3.	$-50 = 5x$	$-100x = 25$	$-9 = 3x$	$-12 = 2x$

D. Solving for x, fractional coefficients. The following is a variation of C:

$\frac{x}{2} = 9$

① In this type of algebra problem, the unknown quantity is being divided.

(2) $\frac{x}{2} = 9$ (2)

② You must multiply $\frac{x}{2}$ by the divisor 2. Then you will have $\frac{2x}{2}$ or x. When you have a fractional part of x, you must multiply to bring its value up to one whole x. Do not forget that multiplying one side of an equation by x is not valid unless you multiply the other side of the equation by the same value.

$$\frac{2x}{2} = 18$$

③ We now have

$x = 18$

④ And the answer is

(12) Perform the multiplication operation in order to solve the following equations:

	(a)	(b)	(c)	(d)
1.	$\frac{x}{5} = 3$	$\frac{x}{4} = 6$	$\frac{x}{-5} = 7$	$\frac{x}{12} = 10$
2.	$\frac{x}{2} = 5$	$\frac{x}{6} = 60$	$\frac{x}{4} = 1$	$\frac{x}{6} = 12$
3.	$\frac{x}{10} = -10$	$\frac{x}{5} = -5$	$\frac{x}{3} = 30$	$\frac{x}{-8} = 11$

9.0 Review of Algebraic Operations

Note 24.1

Combine all like terms—add unknowns to similar unknowns, add number terms to number terms.

Note 25

Isolate unknown terms on one side of the equation.

Note 26

Isolate known terms on the other side of the equation.

Note 27

Perform whatever division or multiplication necessary to reduce the quantity or coefficient of unknowns to become just one whole unknown.

(13)   Perform the necessary algebra steps to solve the following equations. In some examples you will need to perform more than one mathematical operation.

	(a)	*(b)*	*(c)*	*(d)*
1.	$x + 3x = 20$	$x + 5 + x = 7$	$2x + x - x = 12 - 8$	$7 + x = 5 + 2x$
2.	$3x + 5 = 28$	$\dfrac{x}{4} + 5 = 25$	$\dfrac{x}{6} - 7 = 29$	$4x - 5 = 19$
3.	$16 + x = 2x - 8$	$3x + 4 = 55$	$\dfrac{x}{2} + 5 = 17$	$6x + 9 - 2x = 69$
4.	$10x - 0.5 = 1.5$	$\dfrac{3x}{5} = 15$	$\dfrac{2x}{3} - 6 = 3$	$\dfrac{7}{4}x = 56$
5.	$3x - 12 + x = 24$	$0.4x = 40$	$2.5 = x + 1.3$	$1.7x = 3.4$

6. A certain number doubled and increased by 4 equals 12. What is the number?

7. A certain number of coins halved and diminished by 5 equals 4. What is the original amount of coins?

8. A certain group, when tripled and increased by 2, equals 47. What is the number of the original group?

9. If I can accumulate $100 by doubling my money and adding 8 more dollars, how much do I now have?

10. One-quarter of a number is 5 1/2, what is the number?

11. Twice a number plus 3 is 6. What is the number?

12. One-fifth of a number less 1 is 4. What is the number?

13. Ten times a number plus 7 is 92. What is the number?

14. $\dfrac{7}{x} = \dfrac{5}{10}$ $x = \underline{\quad\quad}$

15. $\dfrac{3}{x} = \dfrac{10}{150}$ $x = \underline{\quad\quad}$

16. Three times a number divided by two equals 37.5. What is the original number?

SECTION X
Using Algebra to Solve Formula Problems

1.0 Distance Problems

The G. E. D. Test will contain numerous verbal problems. You will be responsible for reading the problem correctly and solving for the unknown term. Distance problems are concerned with objects travelling at a certain *rate* of speed for a certain period of *time* and covering a certain *distance*.

> *time*—Specific number of days, hours, minutes, seconds, etc., it takes for an object to travel a distance.
>
> *rate*—The charting of distance in time. For example: *miles* per *hour, feet* per *second,* etc.
>
> *distance*—The total amount of space travelled. Distance is charted in miles, feet, inches, etc.

Solving distance problems—In distance problems, you will be given two of the three (distance, rate, and time) variables, and you will be required to solve the problem for the unknown variable. The first question that you must ask yourself when doing any verbal problem is "what is the problem asking for?" You must identify the quantity that is unknown. Then you will know which variable you are to solve for. The distance travelled is equal to the rate of speed times time.

$$\text{Distance} = \text{Rate} \times \text{Time}$$
$$D = RT$$

Suppose you are given a rate and a time in your problem, and you are asked to solve for distance. Use the formula above. Multiplying *rate* times *time* will give you the answer for distance. Example:

If a truck travels for 4 hours at an average speed of 55 miles per hour, how much distance will it cover?

① $D = \text{Rate} \times \text{Time}$
② $D = 55 \times 4$
③ $D = \textbf{220 miles}$ **Ans.**

(1) Solve the following problems for *distance*:

1. $R = 60$, $T = 5$, $D = $ _____?

2. $R = 72$, $T = 3$, $D = $ _____?

3. $R = 70.3$, $T = 3.5$, $D = $ _____?

4. $R = 60$, $T = 3$ hrs. 15 mins., $D = $ _____?

5. $R = 50$, $T = 2$ hrs. 20 mins., $D = $ _____?

6. A bus travels 50 miles per hour. After 3 1/2 hrs., how many miles will the bus have travelled?

7. A plane travels 8 miles a minute. How far will it go in 1 1/2 hours?

8. A man walks 5 miles in one hour. How many miles can he walk in 50 minutes?

9. A car that travels at a rate of 70 m.p.h. will go how far in 1/2 hour?

10. A cyclist travels at 22 m.p.h. How far far can he go in 20 minutes?

2.0 Rate

To find the rate of speed divide the distance travelled by the time taken.

$$\text{Rate} = \text{Distance} \div \text{Time}$$

$$R = \frac{D}{T}$$

If you are given a problem, and you are asked to find rate, when given time and distance, you must divide, according to the above formula. Notice this sample problem:

If a car travels 280 miles in 7 hours, what is the car's rate of speed?

$$R = \frac{Distance}{Time} \qquad R = \frac{280}{7}$$

$$R = 40 \text{ miles per hour}$$

(2) Solve the following problems for rate. Remember to *divide* when looking for *rate*.

    1. $D = 600$, $T = 6$, $R = $ _____?

    2. $T = 5$, $D = 80$, $R = $ _____?

3. A car travels 300 miles in 4 hours. What is the car's rate of speed?

4. A train travels 40 miles in ½ hr., what is the rate of speed of the train?

5. An airplane travels 750 miles in 4 hours. What is the plane's rate of speed?

3.0 Time

To find the time taken divide the distance by the rate.

$$\text{Time} = \text{Distance} \div \text{Rate}$$

$$T = \frac{D}{R}$$

If you are given a problem in which distance and rate are known but time is unknown, you must *divide rate into distance* in order to solve for time. Notice this sample problem:

A car travels 250 miles while travelling at a rate of 50 m.p.h. How long did it take the car to travel this distance?

$$\text{Time} = \frac{\text{Distance}}{\text{Rate}} \qquad T = \frac{250}{50} \qquad T = 5 \text{ hrs.}$$

(3) Solve these problems for *time*. You must divide when you are looking for time.

    1. $R = 70$, $D = 350$, $T = $ _____?

    2. $R = 40$, $D = 180$, $T = $ _____?

3. A car travelling at 40 miles an hour will go thirty miles in what part of an hour?

4. A plane leaves Logan Airport at 5:00 P.M. It must fly 480 miles at the rate of 150 m.p.h. What time will it arrive at its destination?

5. A jet travels at the rate of 400 m.p.h. How long will it take this jet to go 2200 miles?

SECTION XI
Interest Problems

1.0 *Principal*—The principal is that amount of money that is deposited in a bank account, or the amount of money that is drawn from a bank as a loan. The *principal* is also called the *base*.

2.0 *Interest*—The amount of additional money that is usually added to the principal is called the interest. If you hold a savings account, you are given *interest* on the money on deposit. If you take a loan, you pay the loan plus additional money back to the bank in the form of *interest*.

3.0 *Rate*—The percent at which interest is being charged is the interest rate. Interest rate is always computed as a percent of the principal.

4.0 *Time*—The time is the number, or fractional part, of years that the principal is being charged interest.

For example: A man borrows $500 for 2 years at the rate of 10% interest. After the two years, he pays back $600.

$500 represents the man's *principal*
10% represents the *rate of interest*
2 years represents the *time of loan*
$100 represents the *amount of interest* that was paid in addition *to the principal*
$600 represents the total paid

Note 28
Multiply to find the amount of interest.

$$\text{Interest} = \text{principal} \times \text{rate} \times \text{time}$$
$$I = P \times R \times T$$
$$I = PRT$$

Remember that this formula has four variables (items that are changeable) and can be arranged so as to solve for any one of the four variables as shown here:

$P = \dfrac{I}{R} \times T$ *Principal* equals amount of yearly interest divided by rate. This figure is then multiplied by time.

$R = \dfrac{I}{P} \div T$ or $R = \dfrac{\frac{I}{P}}{T}$ *Rate* equals interest divided by *principal*. This rate is then divided by time. All interest rates are based on *one year*.

$T = I \div PR$
or

$T = \dfrac{I}{PR}$ *Time* equals interest divided by principal and rate.

(1) Compute the interest in the following examples, where rate, time, and principal are given:

1. P = $400, R = 5%, T = 1 yr., I = _____?

2. P = $1,000, R = 7%, T = 1 yr., I = _____?

3. P = $2,500, R = 10%, T = 1 yr., I = _____?

4. P = $3,000, R = 5%, T = 3 yrs., I = _____?

5. P = $250, R = 6%, T = 2 yrs., I = _____?

6. P = $500, R = 8%, T = 6 mos., I = _____?

7. P = $8,000, R = 10%, T = 1½ yrs., I = _____?

8. P = $1,000, R = 4½%, T = 2 yrs., I = _____?

9. P = $1,000, R = 5.6%, T = 1.5 yrs., I = _____?

10. P = $4,000, R = 6.1%, T = 3 mos., I = _____?

---

(2) Solve the following interest problems:

1. Mr. Blackwell invests $5,000. At the end of a year, he receives a total of $5,350. What is the annual rate of interest?

2. If Ms. Barker invests $900 at 6% interest for 6 months, how much interest is she entitled to?

3. The Fremont Savings Bank grants 7% interest on all savings above $1,000. For how long must I invest $3,000 before I have $490 in interest?

4. At a bank where the annual rate of interest is 8%, I receive $24 interest after 6 months. What was my principal?

5. A certain bank charges 10% interest on all monies over $2,000. For all monies less than $2,000 the interest rate is 8%. How much interest is charged on monies totalling $5,500?

6. If a 6% annual interest rate is computed, or compounded every ¼ of a year, how much interest is charged every ¼ year?

7. How much principal would net $500 in interest at 5% after 6 months?

8. Which gives more interest, $600 at 6% or $500 at 7% interest?

9. Mr. Perkins invested $2,000 at 6% interest for 2 years and 3 months. How much money can Mr. Perkins withdraw after this time period?

10. If the interest rate in a savings bank is 5.5%, and I deposit $1,700 in the bank, for how long must I invest this money before my total is $2,000?

SECTION XII
Volume and Circular
Area Problems

1.0 Volume Problems

Measurement of a square or rectangular object that also has depth gives the volume of that object. An ice cube, for example, is a square object that has the dimensions of height or length, and width plus a third dimension of depth. The volume of such an object is found by multiplying length times width times depth.

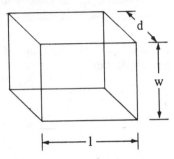

$$V = 1 \times w \times d$$

Volume = length $\times$ width $\times$ depth

Notice in this sample volume problem that *the volume is measured in cubic inches.* Be sure to express your volume answer in cubic units of measure.

Example: Mr. Keller buys an aquarium that is 25 inches long and 16 inches wide. The aquarium is 20 inches deep. What is the volume of Mr. Keller's aquarium?

$$V = 1 \times w \times d$$
$$V = 25 \times 16 \times 20$$
$$V = 8000 \text{ cubic inches}$$

①
$$\begin{array}{r} 25 \\ \times 16 \\ \hline 150 \\ 25 \\ \hline 400 \end{array}$$

②
$$\begin{array}{r} 400 \\ \times 20 \\ \hline 8000 \text{ cubic inches} \end{array}$$

---

(1) Compute the volume in the following problems from the given information:

1. $1 = 14'$, $w = 10'$, $d = 9'$, $V =$ _____ cubic feet

2. $1 = 20'$, $w = 20'$, $d = 20'$, $V =$ _____ cubic feet

3. $1 = 5'$, $w = 2'$, $d = 3'$, $V =$ _____ cubic feet

4. $1 = 8'$, $w = 4'$, $d = 5'$, $V =$ _____ cubic feet

5. $1 = 2.5'$, $w = 5.2'$, $d = 2.2'$, $V =$ _____ cubic feet

6. $1 = 3\frac{1}{4}'$, $w = 2\frac{1}{2}'$, $d = 1\frac{1}{2}'$, $V =$ _____ cubic feet

7. $1 = 5\frac{1}{2}''$, $w = 6''$, $d = 4\frac{2}{3}''$, $V =$ _____ cubic inches

8. $1 = 10.1''$, $w = 9.2''$, $d = 6.6''$, $V =$ _____ cubic inches

9. $1 = 8/3'$, $w = 9/4'$, $d = 7/4'$, $V =$ _____ cubic feet

10. $1 = 60''$, $w = 40''$, $d = 15''$, $V =$ _____ cubic inches

(2) Compute the answer:

1. If the volume of a container equals 240 cubic inches and the length is 10 inches and the width is 6 inches, what is the depth?

2. The volume of a tank equals 1,000 cubic feet. The tank's height, width, and depth are equal. How many feet are contained in the width and depth of this particular tank?

3. A sandbox is 12 ft. long, 8 feet wide and 2 feet deep. What volume of sand is needed to fill the sandbox?

4. Will 500 cubic inches of water be enough to completely fill a tank that is ¾ ft. by 1¼ ft. by ½ ft.?

5. A swimming pool is 25 yards long, 10 yards wide and 2 yards deep. How many cubic feet of water are needed to fill this pool? How many cubic feet of water are needed to fill the pool to 80% of its capacity?

2.0 Circular Area Problems

Recall that the formula for the area of a circle as was given in Section VIII. 1.0, E is:

$A = \pi r^2$, when π equals 22/7 or 3.14

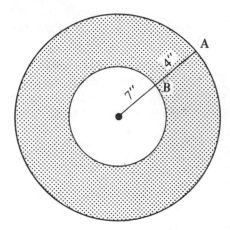

(3) Now apply your knowledge of the area of a circle to the following problems:

1. Ms. Williams buys a circular rug for her kitchen. If the diameter of this rug is 8 feet, how much area can she expect it to cover?

2. The radius of a circular speaking platform is 8 feet. Is it possible to fit two of these platforms on a 30 ft. by 20 ft. stage?

3. In the diagram you see above, the radius of the smaller circle, radius OB is 7″. The distance from point B to point A on the circumference of the larger circle is 4 more inches. What is the area of the smaller circle? What is the area of the shaded portion of the larger circle?

4. On the playing field in the diagram, a circle is constructed with a diameter of 12 yards. The dimensions of the playing field are 50 yds. by 30 yds. How much of the playing field is not included in the circle?

5. By using π as 3.14, I compute a circle with a certain radius to have an area of 113.04 inches. What is the radius of this circle? If I double this radius, what will the area of the circle become?

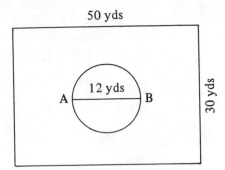

SECTION XIII
Percentage Problems of Discount and Profit

Often merchandisers will have sales where they will offer *discounts*. A discount is often measured in percent. If you buy an item on a particular sale day, you will receive a reduction in price which is a certain percentage of the sale price. In a 10% discount sale, for example, the buyer is in a sense refunded 10% of the sale price. This represents that amount less than the list price, that he does not have to pay, because of the sale.

1.0 *Discount*

percent of discount × selling price = amount of discount

selling price or original price — amount of discount = new price or sale price

---

Note 29

When a discount problem asks for the amount of discount, you must multiply, as indicated above.

Note 30

When a discount problem asks you to compute a sale price based on the discount on the original price, you must multiply to find the amount of discount and then subtract discount from original price to obtain the sale price.

2.0 *Profit*

is computed as a percentage of merchandiser buying price. A dealer may make, for example, a 10% profit based on his own cost price.

Cost price × percent of profit = amount of profit

Cost price + amount of profit = dealer's selling price

Notice the model problems for discount and profit.

Model (A)—*Discount*

A dress that is list priced for $60 is sold at a 20% discount. What is the amount of discount? What is the sale price?

① $60 × 20% = amount of discount
$60 × .20 = $12.00

② $12.00 = amount of discount
$60 — $12 = $48
$48 = sale price

Model (B)—*Profit*

A dealer purchases carpeting for $800. He wishes to make a profit of 40% of his cost. How much profit does he wish to make? What should his selling price be?

① $800 × 40% = amount of profit
$800 × .40 = $320
$320 = amount of profit

② $320 + $800 = $1,120
$1,120 = selling price

(1) Answer the following:

1. If a suit that originally sells for $300 is offered at a "⅓ off" (33⅓%) discount, how much money can you save by buying this suit now?

2. A television set that sells for $120 is put on sale at "⅛ off" price. How much discount is offered on this television set?

3. At a 15% discount, Mr. Smithers buys $225 worth of tools. How much does he pay for these tools?

4. A $500 stereo record player is discounted at 16%. It is then further discounted by 10% more. What is the final sale price for this stereo?

5. A refrigerator that originally sold for $320 is sale priced for $280. What is the rate of discount on this refrigerator?

6. A man buys furniture items at $500. If he wished to make a 12% profit, how much should his selling price be?

7. Mr. Morris pays $1,000 for a shipment of sports jackets. In order to pay for labor, overhead costs, and personal profit, he sells these jackets at 250% of cost. What does he sell them for?

8. Ms. Swift pays $1,600 to the wholesaler for a bedroom set. She wants to fix a price so that she still makes a 15% profit after she offers a 25% discount. What should her list price be?

9. A manufacturer sells a lawn mower that cost him $75 for a 25% profit. The retailer sells it at a 20% profit to Miss Jenkins, his customer. How much does this lawn mower cost the customer?

10. A $50 savings represents a discount on an item of 18%. What was the original selling price for this item?

SECTION XIV
Ratio and Proportion

1.0 *Ratio*

A *ratio* is a comparison of two numbers using division.

If I make $100 a week and my neighbor makes $80 a week, my salary is in a 100/80 (which can be reduced to 5/4) ratio with his salary.

If I am 24 years old, and you are 18 years old our ages are in a 24/18 ratio. This ratio can be reduced to 4/3. This is to say that for each 4 years that my age has, yours has 3 years. In the previous example, for every $5 that I make, my neighbor makes $4.

To find the *ratio* of two numbers, divide the first by the second. If I answer 5 questions right on a test for every 3 questions that you answer right, our correct answers are in a 5/3 ratio. This ratio can be expressed as:

$$5 \text{ to } 3 \text{ } or \text{ } 5{:}3 \text{ } or \text{ } 5/3$$

Whenever you compare two quantities you are finding their ratio.

(1) Write the following ratios as fractions.

	(a)	(b)	(c)
1.	20 to 10	30 to 3	7 to 2
2.	5 to 6	8 to 12	5 to 1
3.	6:3	b:a	x:y
4.	5:5	20 to 5	6 to 2

Remember that, wherever possible, ratios should be reduced, as fractions, to their simplest terms.

For a ratio to be in simplest terms, it should be a ratio of one whole number to another. If two numbers are in the ratio of 2/5 to 2/3, you must divide by fractions. For example:

$$\frac{\frac{2}{5}}{\frac{2}{3}} = \frac{2}{5} \div \frac{2}{3} = \frac{2}{5} \times \frac{3}{2} = \frac{6}{10}$$

ratio in simplest terms, or $\frac{3}{5}$ reduced.

(2) Once a ratio is in simplest form, you may be asked to use it to find actual numbers. This can be seen in the following problems:

1. The ratio of my salary to yours is 6/5. If I make $120 a week, what is your weekly salary?

2. The ratio of the hours Mr. Brown works to the hours Ms. Swanson works is 4/7. If Ms. Swanson works 49 hours a week, how many hours does Mr. Brown work?

3. The ratio of the distance covered by automobile A to automobile B is 8/3. When automobile B has travelled 12 miles, how far has automobile A travelled?

In each of these problems, you are given the basic ratio.

In problem 1, no matter how much our salaries are, our ratio will remain the same.

In problem 2, no matter how much they both work, their ratio will remain the same.

In problem 3, no matter how far both cars travel, their ratio will remain the same.

2.0 *Method for Solving Ratio Problems*

For the solution of ratio problems, the ratio fraction must be set equal to the new proportion that the problem is asking for. In other words, if the ratio of my height to my brother's height is 5:4, this ratio is set as a fraction and used in the problem solution as:

① $\frac{5}{4}$

Now, if the problem information states that I am 65 inches tall, this fact is represented in a fraction across from the original ratio number that represents my height as follows:

(2) $\frac{5}{4} = \frac{65}{\underline{}}$

x is used to represent my brother's actual height. This is what you will be required to solve for:

	basic ratio		actual height
(3)	$\frac{5}{4}$	=	$\frac{65}{x}$

By cross multiplying diagonally, you can restate this equation and then solve it.

(4) $\frac{5}{4} \diagup\!\!\!\!\diagdown \frac{65}{x}$ $5x = 260$
                       $x = 52$ inches

Notice the following model problems:

(A) The ratio of my salary to yours is 6:5. If I make $120 a week, what is your weekly salary?

   (1) $\frac{6}{5} = \frac{120}{x}$
   (2) $6x = \$600$
   (3) $x = \$100$ salary

(B) The ratio of the distance covered by automobile A to automobile B is 8:3. When automobile B has travelled 12 miles, how far has automobile A travelled?

   (1) $\frac{8}{3} = \frac{x}{12}$
   (2) $3x = 96$
   (3) $x = 32$ miles

When ratio problems present you with the proportions of two men or three men as regards a total, then the problem is set up in terms of x. Note model (C).

(C) Three men divide a company's profit in a 5:3:2 ratio. If the profits are $60,000, how much is each man's share?

Set x equal to one ratio part. However, since none of the three men are in a 1 part ratio, 2x will represent the portion of the man who makes the least. 3x will represent the next man and 5x will represent the man who holds the biggest share of the profits.

(1) $5x + 3x + 2x = \$60,000$
(2) $10x = \$60,000$
(3) $x = \$6,000 =$ one ratio part
(4) $5x = \$30,000 =$ first man
(5) $3x = \$18,000 =$ second man
(6) $2x = \$12,000 =$ third man

(3) Solve the following ratio problems:

1. In a classroom, the ratio of girls to boys is 4 to 3. If there are 15 boys in the class, how many girls are there?

2. In a recipe, milk is to be added to flour in a 5 to 2 ratio. If 2.5 cups of milk are used, how much flour should be added?

3. If Ms. Bowman's age is a 3:2 ratio with her daughter's age, and her daughter is 40 years old, then how old is Ms. Bowman?

4. If Mr. Winston's sales are in a 7:3 ratio with Mr. Abbot's sales, and Mr. Abbot's sales are $15,000, then what are Mr. Winston's sales?

5. A scale of miles indicates Franklin is 2/5 of an inch away and Boston is 2/3 of an inch away. If Franklin is 3 miles away, then how far away is Boston?

6. Two partners split the cost of materials in a 6:5 ratio. If the total cost is $44,-000, how much does each man pay?

7. Three passengers split long distance driving time in a 5:2:1 proportion. If the total driving time is 60 hours, how much time did each passenger spend driving?

SECTION XV
Graphs

In this section, you will be shown how to read and interpret the three basic types of graphs. While graphs are not numerical, they often do measure statistics and numerical quantities.

The three basic graphs are:

A. The *circle graph,* or the *pie graph*
B. The *linear graph*
C. The *bar graph*

A. The *circle* graph

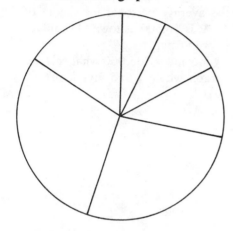

A circle graph uses the circle to show the size or amount of what is being graphed. Once the circle is split into sectors, each sector measures one item for the graph. In this way the relative amount of each item can be seen in comparison to the others.

Middletown Budget 1958

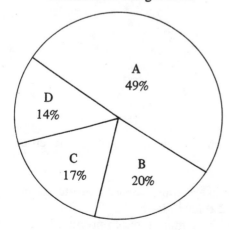

Key: A = Building and construction outlay

B = Salaries of public officials

C = Repairs and renewal

D = Miscellaneous expenses

By studying the graph and using the key, you should be able to answer any question based on this graph.

117

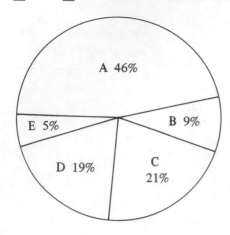

Personal Income breakdown of Town "D"

Key: A = income between $10,000 and $20,000
  B = income over $20,000
  C = income between $8,000 and $10,000
  D = income between $3,000 and $8,000
  E = income less than $3,000

(1) Do the following problems:

1. Based on the preceding graph, the majority of the residents of town "D" earn _____.

2. The smallest group of people in town "D" earn _____.

3. If the average personal income in the U. S. A. is $6,500, is town "D" affluent or poor in comparison?

4. If my income is $35,000 what sector of the graph would I find myself in?

Percentage of Farm Products Grown—
U. S. A. 1962

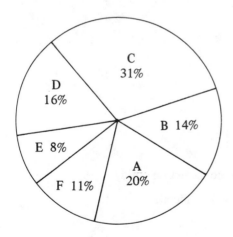

Crop breakdown —— leading crops

Key: A = tobacco
  B = cotton
  C = grain
  D = citrus
  E = lettuce
  F = potato

Can you determine the *amount* of cotton that was produced in 1962?

Can you determine the *percentage* of grain that was harvested in 1964?

The title of the graph will tell you what the graph is concerned with, what it is measured in, and what time period is being considered.

(2) Answer the following based on the crop graph.

1. Was there more tobacco produced in 1962 than cotton?

2. Was there more tobacco produced than grain?

3. The ratio of citrus produced to lettuce produced is _____?

4. What two products, taken together, constitute over half of our nation's farm produce?

5. 16% of our farm produce constitutes what one crop?

B. The *linear* graph (line graph)
A linear graph has a vertical axis and a horizontal axis. Each axis measures a different variable, and the student will have to study both axes to get a clear picture of what is being graphed.

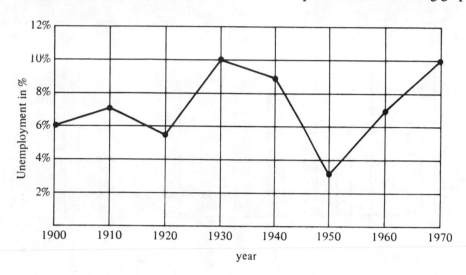

year

(3) Notice in the preceding graph the trend of unemployment. Has unemployment been constant or has it varied? What have been the years of greatest unemployment? What was the year of greatest employment? Remember that the depression occurred during the 1930's. Remember that WWII occurred during the early 1940's. What facts does this graph bear out about the depression? and WWII?

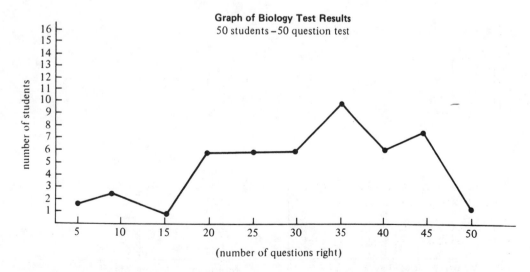

Graph of Biology Test Results
50 students – 50 question test

(number of questions right)

(4) How many students answered all questions correctly?

What trends will this graph show an instructor about his class in relation to this test?

C. The *bar* graph
    Bar graphs also employ a vertical and horizontal axis just as linear graphs do.

It will be easier for you to see comparisons and contrast patterns in a bar graph.

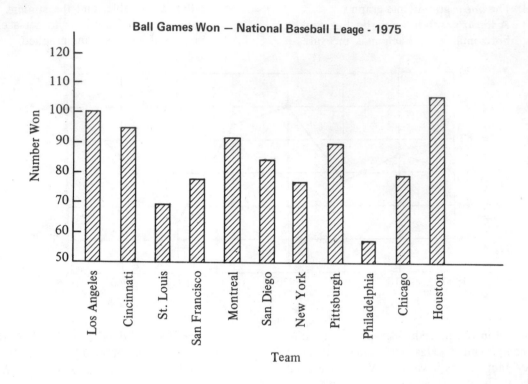

Ball Games Won — National Baseball Leage - 1975

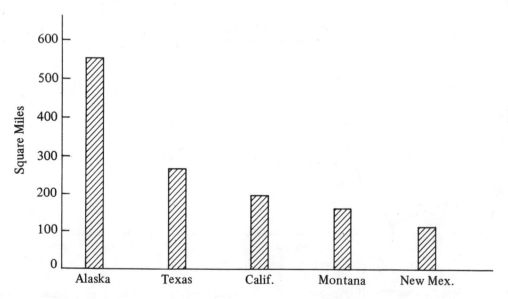

(5)   Area of the five largest states in the U.S.A. Approximately how large is the state of California? What is the approximate ratio of Alaska's size to Texas's size?

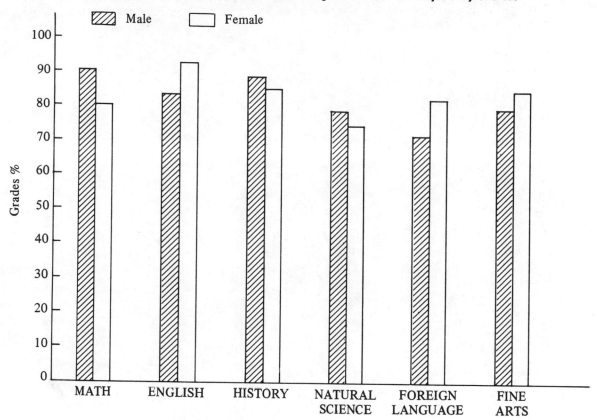

Comparison of Male and Female Grade - High School A - six major subject areas

(6) What is the worst male subject area?
What is the best female subject area?

In what subject area is the male–female achievement level most nearly the same?

SIMULATED G.E.D. MATHEMATICS EXAMINATION

USE THE SPECIAL PENCIL.   MAKE GLOSSY BLACK MARKS.

	A	B	C	D	E			A	B	C	D	E
1							26					
2							27					
3							28					
4							29					
5							30					
6							31					
7							32					
8							33					
9							34					
10							35					

Make only ONE mark for each answer.   Additional and stray marks may be counted as mistakes.   In making corrections, erase errors COMPLETELY.

	A	B	C	D	E			A	B	C	D	E
11							36					
12							37					
13							38					
14							39					
15							40					
16							41					
17							42					
18							43					
19							44					
20							45					
21							46					
22							47					
23							48					
24							49					
25							50					

1. The area of the rectangle is

9 INCHES

1½ FT

a) 172 sq. inches
b) 202 sq. inches
c) 13 1/2 sq. inches
d) 162 sq. inches
e) none of the above

2. Which number is the largest

a) 29/13
b) 2
c) 2.6
d) 2 1/3
e) 35/15

3. $-1\ 5/8 - 2\ 3/5 =$ _____

a) $-4\ 9/40$
b) $2\ 1/20$
c) $-39/40$
d) $4\ 9/40$
e) none of the above

4. If $4! = 4\cdot3\cdot2\cdot1 = 24$ (4! is read as 4 factorial and is $= 4 \times 3 \times 2 \times 1 = 24$),

find $\dfrac{6!}{3!}$

a) 120   c) 15   e) 2
b) 40   d) 6

5. A student received grades of 92, 87, 77, 83, and 90. What was his average?

a) 81 2/5
b) 86
c) 85 4/5
d) 82 4/5
e) none of the above

6. A right triangle has legs measuring 8″ and 13″. Find the area.

a) 52 sq. in.
b) 104 sq. in.
c) 42 sq. in.
d) 21 sq. in.
e) none of the above

7. $.05 \times 120 =$

a) 12
b) 1.2
c) .6
d) 6.0
e) 60

8. In the rectangle below, find the length of the diagonal.

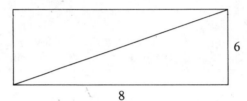

6

8

a) 10
b) 12
c) 9
d) 8
e) 11

9. If Jack is 5 years older than his sister, and together their ages equal 37, how old is Jack's sister?

a) 10
b) 15
c) 16
d) 14
e) none of the above

10. The area of a square is 432 sq. in. How many sq. ft. is it?

a) 6
b) 3
c) 216
d) 12
e) 36

125

11. $\dfrac{18}{9} = \dfrac{44}{x}$ What does x equal?

    a) 16
    b) 90
    c) 30
    d) 35
    e) 22

12. Simplify:

    $4m + (5m) - (8m)$

    a) 17m   d) 7m
    b) m   e) —m
    c) —9m

13. A large box is $2' \times 2' \times 4''$. How many smaller boxes each $4'' \times 4'' \times 1'$ will it hold?

    a) 62
    b) 144
    c) 72
    d) 1
    e) none of these

14. What % of 80 is 16?

    a) 25%
    b) 40%
    c) 33 1/3%
    d) 35%
    e) 20%

15. $\sqrt{.04} =$

    a) .2
    b) .02
    c) .04
    d) 2
    e) none of the above

16. 3 men divide a work hour load in a 1:4:5 ratio. If 200 work hours are completed, how many hours are worked by the man who works most?

    a) 80 hours
    b) 40 hours
    c) 30 hours
    d) 100 hours
    e) 50 hours

NUMBER OF ANNUAL MILES DRIVEN
(Questions 17-19)

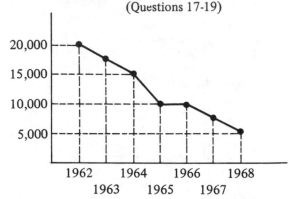

17. What is the total amount of miles driven? (1962-1968 inclusive)

    a) 60,000
    b) 85,000
    c) 92,000
    d) 70,000
    e) 65,500

18. In the graph above what is the ratio in simplest terms of the miles driven in 1962 to the miles driven in 1968?

    a) 6:3
    b) 5:1
    c) 4:1
    d) 20:5
    e) 3:1

19. What is the average number of yearly miles driven? Choose best answer rounded off to the nearest mile.

    a) 13,150
    b) 12,143
    c) 12,402
    d) 13,074
    e) 11,010

20. If the area of a circle is 36 sq. in., how many sq. ft. is it?

    a) 3 sq. ft.   c) .25 sq. ft.
    b) 2.5 sq. ft.   d) 25 sq. ft.

21. 60 is 15% of what number?

    a) 200   c) 120
    b) 360   d) 400

22. If the $f(x) = 4x + 4$, then $f(4) - f(2) =$

    a) 6   c) 8
    b) 12   d) 20

23. A swimming pool is 120 ft. long and 30 ft. wide. It has a depth of 5 ft. How many gallons will it hold if each cubic ft. is equal to 6.5 gallons?

    a) 120,000
    b) 117,000
    c) 200,500
    d) 18,000
    e) none of the above

24. 130% of 130 is

    a) 169
    b) 160.9
    c) 130
    d) 16.9
    e) none of the above

25. Mr. Johnson invests a certain amount of money at 6% interest for a year. At the end of the year he receives 120 dollars in interest. How much money did he invest?

    a) $2500
    b) $2300
    c) $1800
    d) $2100
    e) none of the above

26. Solve for y: $\dfrac{3y}{2} - 18 = \dfrac{-y}{2}$

    a) $y = 5$
    b) $y = 6.5$

    c) $y = 4.5$
    d) $y = 3/2$
    e) $y = 9$

27. If triangle ABC is a right triangle what is the length of side AB?

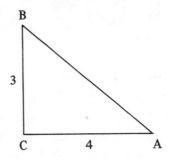

    a) 5
    b) 4
    c) 6
    d) 2
    e) none of the above

28. If $F(x,y,z) = 2x - 3y + 4z$
    then $F(1,-2,3) =$

    a) x,y,z
    b) 18
    c) 20
    d) 3
    e) 19

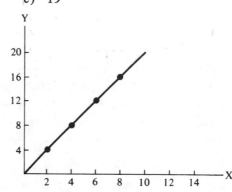

29. In order to keep this graph constant:

    a) x and y must decrease
    b) y must double x
    c) x must double y
    d) x must not exceed 30
    e) none of the above

30. John's rate of driving speed is 60 m.p.h. and Phil's rate is 50 m.p.h. If they leave from the same point but travel in opposite directions, how far apart will they be after traveling half an hour?

    a) 110 miles
    b) 55 miles
    c) 60 miles
    d) 220 miles
    e) none of the above

31. A merchant spends 72 dollars to market an item. He makes a profit of 18 dollars. What is his percent of profit?

    a) 40%
    b) 20%
    c) 25%
    d) 33 1/3%

32. What is the equivalent of 1.3652×10^3?

    a) 13.652
    b) 13,652
    c) 1,365.2
    d) 136.52

Sq. ft. of Pavement	2000	4000	8000
Pounds of Cement	40	80	160

33. According to the data in the table above, how many pounds are needed to make 7,500 sq. ft. of pavement?

    a) 140 lbs.
    b) 160 lbs.
    c) 165 lbs.
    d) 150 lbs.
    e) none of the above

34. In the formula $XY = B$: What is the effect on B if X is doubled and Y remains the same?

    a) B doubles
    b) B triples
    c) B becomes one half as large
    d) B remains the same

35. If butter costs $.46 a pound, what will 3 1/2 lbs. of butter cost?

    a) $1.50
    b) $1.71
    c) $1.46
    d) $1.55
    e) $1.61

36. If one angle of a triangle equals 42 degrees, and the other two angles are equal, how many degrees does each angle contain?

    a) 72°
    b) 45°
    c) 90°
    d) 69°
    e) none of the above

37. A circle with a radius of 6″ has a circumference of

    a) 12π
    b) 6π
    c) 18π
    d) 10π
    e) 20π

PRICE TABLE FOR CLOTH "A" AND "B"

	10 sq. ft.	100 sq. ft.	1000 sq. ft.
A	$2.00	$20.00	$200
B	$3.00	$30.00	$300

(Questions 38-40 are based on this chart.)

38. What is the cost of 750 sq. ft. of carpet "A"?

    a) $130
    b) $150
    c) $175
    d) $180
    e) none of the above

39. What is the ratio of the price of cloth "B" to an equal amount of cloth "A"?

    a) 2:3
    b) 1:2
    c) 3:2
    d) 3:5
    e) none of the above

40. How much of cloth "B" can be bought for the price of 300 sq. ft. of cloth "A"?

    a) 100 sq. ft.
    b) 200 sq. ft.
    c) 250 sq. ft.
    d) 1000 sq. ft.

41. A 38-gallon mixture of water and alcohol contains 16 gallons of alcohol. What is the percentage of water in this mixture, rounded off to the nearest percent?

    a) 56%
    b) 58%
    c) 42%
    d) 41%
    e) 40%

42. If the rental fee for a small boat is $1.80 per hour, what is the charge for a boat that is rented from 8:45 AM to 1:00 PM?

    a) $7.00
    b) $6.25
    c) $8.75
    d) $7.65
    e) none of the above

43. The scale of miles on a map is $1/4'' = 10$ miles. A distance of 60 miles is

    a) $2''$
    b) $1\,1/2''$
    c) $1''$
    d) $1\,1/4''$
    e) $1\,3/4''$

44. Given the formula $\dfrac{C}{A} = H$: solving for A

    a) $A = HC$

    b) $A = \dfrac{C}{H}$

    c) $A = \dfrac{H}{C}$

    d) $A = HC - H$

45. If the ceiling of a room is 15 ft. by 10 ft., how many gallons of paint are required to paint the ceiling, if one gallon of paint covers 25 sq. ft.?

    a) 6 gallons
    b) 5 gallons
    c) 8 gallons
    d) 4 gallons
    e) 7 gallons

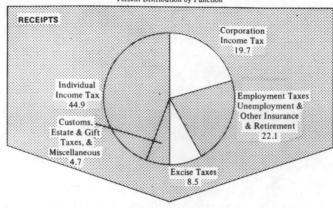

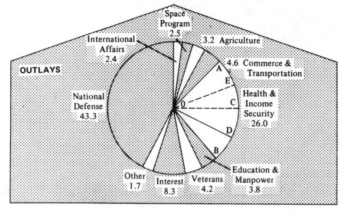

46. How much of the total receipts were received from individual and corporate income taxes? (Rounded off to the nearest percent.)

    a) 60%
    b) 65%
    c) 67%
    d) 63%

47. The ratio of individual income tax to corporate tax, rounded off to the nearest whole number is:

    a) 4:10
    b) 10:4
    c) 9:4
    d) 4:9

48. National defense and health and income security accounts for approximately how much of the total outlay?

    a) 68%
    b) 69%
    c) 47%
    d) 48%

49. The income from excise taxes most nearly equals the outlay for

    a) international affairs plus space program
    b) commerce and transportation
    c) interest
    d) agriculture

50. Which of the following angles best represents an outlay of 14% for health and income security

    a) Angle AoD
    b) Angle AoC
    c) Angle AoB
    d) Angle AoE

G.E.D.T. MINIMUM REQUIREMENTS

Information About Applying for the GED Tests

NOTE – The information in these charts was up-to-date as of the time that this book was printed.

– Information was taken from *State Department of Education Policies, Issuance of High School Certificates Based on GED Test Results.* Bulletin Number 5, Eleventh Edition, June 1972. Commission on Accreditation of Service Experiences, American Council on Education, Washington, D.C.

– Because the rules change occasionally, you should check before you apply for the tests. See the offices and addresses in the charts.

– The chart is organized in two sections: the fifty-six United States areas, and the five Canadian provinces.

UNITED STATES

PLACE	OFFICE AND ADDRESS	MINIMUM AGE	RESIDENCE	MINIMUM SCORES
Alabama	Supervisor of Instruction State Dept. of Education State Office Building 501 Dexter Avenue Montgomery, Alabama 36104	18	30 days	35 on each test *or* 45 average on five tests
Alaska	Commissioner of Education State Dept. of Education Pouch F Alaska Office Building Juneau, Alaska 99801	6 months after time your class would have graduated	30 days	35 on each test *or* 45 average on five tests
American Samoa	Director of Education Department of Education Government of American Samoa Pago Pago, Tutuila American Samoa 96920	19, and your class must have graduated	Must be resident	35 on each test
Arizona	State Director of Adult Education State Department of Education 1626 West Washington Street Phoenix, Arizona 85007	17, and out of school for one year	Must be resident	35 on each test *and* 45 average on five tests
Arkansas	Associate Director for Instructional Services State Dept. of Education State Education Building Little Rock, Arkansas 72201	18, and out of school one year	30 days	35 on each test *or* 45 average on five tests
California*	Chief Bureau of School Approvals State Dept. of Education 721 Capitol Mall Sacramento, California 95814	*	*	35 on each test* *and* 45 average on five tests
Canal Zone	Canal Zone College Box 3009 Balboa, Canal Zone	19	Must be resident	40 on each test *and* 45 average on five tests

State	Address	Age Requirement	Residency	Minimum Test Score[1]
Colorado	Asst. Director, Improved Learning Unit State Dept. of Education State Office Building 201 E. Colfax Denver, Colorado 80203	18	Must be resident	35 on each test *and* 45 average on five tests
Connecticut	Adult Education Consultant State Dept. of Education Box 2219 Hartford, Connecticut 06115	18, and your class must have graduated	Must be resident	35 on each test *and* 45 average on five tests
Delaware	State Supervisor of High School Extension State Department of Public Instruction Townsend Building Dover, Delaware 19901	17, and your class must have graduated	6 months	40 on each test *and* 45 average on five tests
District of Columbia	Armstrong Adult Education Center 1st and O Streets, N.W. Washington, D.C. 20001	17, and out of school for one year	Must be resident	35 on each test *and* 45 average on five tests
Florida	Director, Adult and Veteran Education State Dept. of Education Knott Building Tallahassee, Florida 32304	18, and out of school 6 months	Must be resident	40 on each test *and* 45 average on five tests
Georgia	Coordinator, Adult Education Unit State Dept. of Education 156 Trinity Avenue S.W. Atlanta, Georgia 30303	18	Must be resident	35 on each test *and* 45 average on five tests
Guam	Deputy Director of Instruction Dept. of Education P.O. Box DE Agana, Guam 96910	17, and your class must have graduated	Not required	35 on each test *and* 45 average on five tests
Hawaii	State Program Admin. Adult Education Section Dept. of Education 1270 Queen Emma Street Honolulu, Hawaii 96813	18, and your class must have graduated	Must be resident	35 on each test *and* 45 average on five tests

*State Department of Education does not issue an equivalency certificate. Decision made by local district.
[1] Minimum requirements vary from state to state. Refer to Appendix I. for a complete description.

PLACE	OFFICE AND ADDRESS	MINIMUM AGE	RESIDENCE	MINIMUM SCORES
Idaho	Director, Auxiliary Services State Department of Education State Office Building Boise, Idaho 83707	18, and special permission	6 months	45 on each test
Illinois	Director, Department of Adult Education Office of the Superintendent of Public Instruction 316 South Second Street Springfield, Illinois 62706	19, and out of school one year	1 year	35 on each test *and* 45 average on five tests
Indiana	Director, Division of Adult Education State Dept. of Public Instruction 100 North Senate Avenue Indianapolis, Indiana 46204	19, and out of school a year, and your class has graduated	6 months	35 on each test *and* 45 average on five tests
Iowa	Guidance Services Section State Department of Education Grimes State Office Building Des Moines, Iowa 50319	One year after your class has graduated	Not required	40 on each test *and* 45 average on five tests
Kansas	Adult Education Section State Department of Kansas State Education Building 120 E. 10th Street Topeka, Kansas 66612	18, and your class must have graduated	6 months	35 on each test *and* 45 average on five tests
Kentucky	Division of Adult Education State Dept. of Education Frankfort, Kentucky 40601	17, and your class must have graduated	Must be resident	35 on each test *and* 45 average on five tests
Louisiana*	Supervisor of Secondary Education State Dept. of Education P.O. Box 44064 Baton Rouge, Louisiana 70804	18	Must be resident	35 on each test *or* 45 average on five tests
Maine	State Director of Adult Education State Dept. of Education Education Building Augusta, Maine 04330	18, and out of school one year	6 months	35 on each test *and* 45 average on five tests

State	Address	Age Requirement	Residency	Test Score Requirement
Maryland	Supervisor in Accreditation State Dept. of Education State Office Building 301 West Preston Street Room 1007 Baltimore, Maryland 21201	17 and out of school 6 months	1 year	40 on each test *and* 45 average on five tests
Massachusetts	Bureau of Adult Education State Dept. of Education 182 Tremont Street Boston, Massachusetts 02111	19, and your class must have graduated	6 months	35 on each test *and* 45 average on five tests
Michigan	Coordinator of Adult Education State Dept. of Education Lansing, Michigan 48902	18, and your class must have graduated	Not required	35 on each test *and* 45 average on five tests
Minnesota	Director, Secondary Education State Dept. of Education Capitol Square Building Room 682 St. Paul, Minnesota 55101	19	Must be resident	35 on each test *and* 45 average on five tests
Mississippi	State Supervisor of Adult Education State Dept. of Education P. O. Box 771 Jackson, Mississippi 39205	18	Must be resident	40 on each test *or* 45 on five tests
Missouri	Director, General Adult Education State Dept. of Education Box 480, Jefferson Building Jefferson City, Missouri 65101	18, and out of school 6 months	Must be resident	35 on each test *and* 45 average on five tests
Montana	Supervisor, Adult Basic Education Office of State Superintendent of Public Instruction Montana State Capitol Building Helena, Montana 59601	17, and out of school for one year	Must be resident	35 on each test *or* 45 average on five tests
Nebraska	Administrator, High School Equivalency State Dept. of Education 233 South 10th Street Lincoln, Nebraska 68508	17, and out of school for one year	30 days	40 on each test *or* 45 average on five tests

*State Department of Education does not issue an equivalency certificate. Decision made by local district.

PLACE	OFFICE AND ADDRESS	MINIMUM AGE	RESIDENCE	MINIMUM SCORES
Nevada*	Assoc. Superintendent, Div. 21 of Operations State Dept. of Education Carson City, Nevada 89701	18, or your class must have graduated	Must be resident	35 on each test *and* 45 average on five tests
New Hampshire	Chief, Division of Instruction State Dept. of Education State House Annex Concord, New Hampshire 03301	18, or your class must have graduated	Must be resident	35 on each test *and* 45 average on five tests
New Jersey	Director, High School Equivalency State Dept. of Education P.O. Box 2019 107 West State Street Trenton, New Jersey 08625	18, and out of school for one year	Must be resident	35 on each test *and* 45 average on five tests
New Mexico	Director, Adult Basic Education State Dept. of Education Education Building Santa Fe, New Mexico 87501	18, and your class must have graduated	Must be resident	40 on each test *or* 50 average on five tests
New York	Bureau of Higher and Professional Educational Testing State Education Department Albany, New York 12224	17, and your class must have graduated	Must be resident	35 on each test *and* 45 average on five tests
North Carolina	State GED Administrator State Board of Education Raleigh, North Carolina 27602	18	Must be resident	35 on each test *and* 45 average on five tests
North Dakota	Administrative Assistant State Department of Public Instruction Bismarck, North Dakota 58501	19	Must be resident	40 on each test *or* 50 average on five tests
Ohio	Consultant, Adult Guidance and GED Testing State Dept. of Education 751 Northwest Boulevard Columbus, Ohio 43212	17, and out of school one year	Must be resident	40 on each test *and* 48 average on five tests
Oklahoma	Administrator of Adult Education State Dept. of Education State Capitol Building Oklahoma City, Oklahoma 73105	19	Must be resident	35 on each test *and* 45 average on five tests

State		Age / School Requirement	Residency	Test Score Requirement
Oregon	Coordinator of GED Testing Division of Student Services Oregon Board of Education 942 Lancaster Drive, N.E. Salem, Oregon 97310	18, and your class must have graduated	Must be resident	40 on each test
Pennsylvania	Director, Bureau of Pupil Personnel Services Department of Education Box 911 Harrisburg, Pennsylvania 17126	18	3 months	35 on each test *and* 45 average on five tests
Puerto Rico	Director, Division of Secondary Education P.O. Box 1028 Hato Rey, Puerto Rico 00919	18, and out of school for a year	Must be resident	50 average on five tests *or* 1-36, 2-42, 3-44, 4-38, 5-46
Rhode Island	Coordinator, Adult Education State Dept. of Education Roger Williams Building Hayes Street Providence, Rhode Island 02908	19, and out of school 6 months *or* 18, and class must have graduated for 6 months	Must be resident	35 on each test *and* 45 average on five tests
South Carolina	Chief Supervisor Secondary Education State Dept. of Education Room 808, Rutledge Bldg. Columbia, South Carolina 29201	19	Must be resident	45 average on five tests
South Dakota	Director of Special Services State Department of Public Instruction Pierre, South Dakota 57501	Your class must have graduated	Must be resident	35 on each test *or* 45 average on five tests
Tennessee	Director, Program Development (Secondary) State Dept. of Education 140 Cordell Hull Building Nashville, Tennessee 37219	17, and out of school 6 months	Must be resident	45 average on five tests
Texas	Commissioner for Teacher Education and Institutional Services Texas Education Agency 201 East 11th Street Austin, Texas 78701	17	Must be resident	40 on each test *or* 45 average on five tests

*State Department of Education does not issue an equivalency certificate. Decision made by local district.

PLACE	OFFICE AND ADDRESS	MINIMUM AGE	RESIDENCE	MINIMUM SCORES
Trust Territory of Pacific Islands	Supervisor, Secondary Education Headquarters, Dept. of Education Trust Territory of Pacific Islands Saipan, Mariana Islands 96950	18	3 months	35 on each test
Utah*	Division of Adult Education and Training State Board of Education 136 East South Temple Street Salt Lake City, Utah 84111	17, and special permission	Must be resident	40 on each test *and* 45 average on five tests
Vermont	Director, Division of Teacher and Continuing Education State Dept. of Education Montpelier, Vermont 05602	16	Must be resident	35 on each test *and* 45 average on five tests
Virginia	Supervisor of Adult Education State Board of Education 1322-28 East Grace Street Richmond, Virginia 23216	Your class must have graduated	6 months	35 on each test *and* 45 average on five tests
Washington	Director of Adult Education Division of Curriculum and Instruction Office of Superintendent of Public Instruction P. O. Box 527 Olympia, Washington 98504	18	Must be resident	35 on each test *and* 45 average on five tests
West Virginia	Bureau of Instruction and Curriculum State Dept. of Education Capitol Building, 1900 Washington Street, E. Charleston, West Virginia 25305	17, and out of school for 6 months	Must be resident	35 on each test *or* 45 average on five tests
Wisconsin	Administrator, Instructional Services Division State Department of Public Instruction Wisconsin Hall, 126 Langdon Street Madison, Wisconsin 53702	17	Must be resident	35 on each test *and* 45 average on five tests
Wyoming	Director, Licensing and Certification Unit State Dept. of Education State Capitol Building Cheyenne, Wyoming 82001	17, and out of school for one year	Must be resident	35 on each test *and* 45 average on five tests

*State Department of Education does not issue an equivalency certificate. Decision made by local district.

CANADA

PLACE	OFFICE AND ADDRESS	MINIMUM AGE	RESIDENCE	MINIMUM SCORES
Manitoba	Administrator, Planning and Research Department of Education Winnipeg, Manitoba	19, out of school one year, class must have graduated	6 months	35 on each test *and* 45 average on five tests
New Brunswick	Director of Pupil Personnel Services Department of Education Centennial Building Fredericton, New Brunswick	18, out of school one year, class must have graduated	Not required	35 on each test *and* 45 average on five tests
Nova Scotia	Asst. Director, Youth Education Department of Education P.O. Box 578 Halifax, Nova Scotia	19, out of school one year, class must have graduated	6 months	35 on each test *and* 45 average on five tests
Prince Edward Island	Director of Elementary and Secondary Education Department of Education Charlottetown, P.E.I.	19, out of school one year, class must have graduated	6 months	35 on each test *and* 45 average on five tests
Saskatchewan	Chief, Student Evaluation and Registrar Department of Education, Avord Tower Regina, Saskatchewan	19, out of school one year	6 months	40 on each test *and* 45 average on five tests

ANSWER KEYS

DIAGNOSTIC MATH TEST PROBLEM ANSWERS (from page 3)

1. c	**7.** b	**13.** a	**19.** a	**25.** b	**31.** b
2. b	**8.** d	**14.** c	**20.** c	**26.** d	**32.** a
3. a	**9.** b	**15.** b	**21.** a	**27.** b	**33.** c
4. d	**10.** a	**16.** c	**22.** b	**28.** b	**34.** d
5. b	**11.** d	**17.** 15	**23.** a	**29.** d	**35.** b
6. b	**12.** b	**18.** c	**24.** b	**30.** b	

SECTION I. 1.0 ANSWER KEY (from pages 13 and 14)

(1)
a) 9, 9, 11, 12, 14, 13, 11, 6, 14, 15
b) 30, 60, 73, 165, 100, 88, 69, 133, 117, —
c) 718, 565, 687, 804, 407, 748, 1360, 1469, —, —
d) 7542, 15,252, 7676, 8395, 3337, 3063, 9709, —, —, —

(2)

	(a)	(b)	(c)	(d)	(e)
1)	18,	20,	21,	10,	11
2)	42,	38,	40,	38,	121
3)	156,	151,	90,	172,	628
4)	3451,	8899,	589,	637,	671
5)	1451				
6)	1483				
7)	1019				
8)	$146.04				
9)	1369				
10)	1530				

(3)
a) 11   f) $1714.00
b) 33   g) 158
c) 117   h) 124
d) 46   i) 408
e) $71.00

(4)
a) 584, 1018, 31, 104, 210, 181, 1340, 434
b) 880
c) 205
d) 215
e) 141

(5)
1) 52   6) 1215
2) 123   7) 848
3) 36   8) 69
4) 2045   9) 683
5) 154   10) 68

SECTION I. 2.0 ANSWER KEY (from page 16)

(1) a)   4,   5,   2,   4,   1,   4,   3,   2,   6,   6
    b)   17,   16,   13,   4,   17,   8,   31,   4, 32
    c)   46,   12,   31, 202, 100, 269, 215, 524
    d) 760, 411, 189, 3123, 1246, 5240, 4431

(2) a) 2784   g) $ 4500
    b)   248   h)   1949
    c)   5   i) $ 4
    d)   200   j)   283
    f) 11,612
    e)   321

	(a)	(b)	(c)	(d)	(e)
(3) 1)	51	38	7	58	76
2)	2	8	10	36	25
3)	18	74	110	121	454
4)	100	730	566	90	389
5)	618	686	74621	286	50,108
6)	375				
7)	145				
8)	59				
9)	69				
10)	8769		13) 9995		
11)	73,790		14) 130		
12)	1500		15) 692		

(4) 1)   258   6)   481
    2) 1024   7) 9954
    3)   35   8)   34
    4)   26   9)   266
    5) 4368   10)   35

SECTION I. 3.0 ANSWER KEY (from page 18)

(1) a)   54,   21,   48,   9,   0,   8
    b) 297,   368,   153,   224,   996,   3366
    c) 3672, 12172, 729624,   73080,   40880

(2) a)   30   e)   51   i) 320
    b) 540   f) 416   j) 207
    c) 2016   g) 210
    d) 1001   h) $171

(from page 21)

		(a)	(b)	(c)	(d)	(e)
(3)	1)	486,	100,	292,	186,	235
	2)	486,	198,	300,	434,	328
	3)	935,	864,	1456,	1674,	3600
	4)	825,	1344,	1971,	7245,	7946
	5)	9951,	11,178,	11,200,	10,700,	6210
	6)	621,000,	72,000,	600,000,	612,500,	2,643,500
	7)	26,311,	25,000,	61,500,	177,000,	356,000

8)	165	9)	1364	10)	20,460	11)	11,740
12)	50,000	13)	780,000	14)	37,200	15)	10,512

(4)	1)	1064	4)	576	7)	72,000
	2)	74,000	5)	3787	8)	1152
	3)	1728	6)	10,368		

SECTION I. 4.0 ANSWER KEY (from pages 23 and 24)

(1)	a)	2,	5,	31,	11
	b)	4,	25,	3,	21
	c)	0.05,	0.003,	.0049	10
	d)	0.05,	0.33,	.083	
	e)	342,	220,	11,	

(2)	a)	105	f)	25
	b)	100	g)	$31,000
	c)	4	h)	2
	d)	0	i)	12
	e)	31	j)	108

(3)		(a)	(b)	(c)	(d)
	1)	40	40	701	83
	2)	100	750	551	35
	3)	36	26	323	26
	4)	162	301	37	47
	5)	31	802	48	27
	6)	300	4	40	1004
	7)	20	1	10	24
	8)	625	176	12	223
	9)	39			
	10)	401			
	11)	33			
	12)	81			
	13)	42			
	14)	2000			
	15)	1110			

SECTION II. ANSWER KEY   (from page 27)

(1)	a) 105		f)	28
	b) 7		g)	233
	c) 8		h)	4
	d) 124		i)	86.4
	e) 118		j)	$1.08

MASTERY TEST ANSWER KEY   (from pages 27 and 28)

I	1)	13	2)	15	III	33)	54	34)	35
	3)	9	4)	9		35)	48	36)	28
	5)	165	6)	69		37)	224	38)	352
	7)	133	8)	117		39)	996	40)	3366
	9)	565	10)	804		41)	12,172	42)	733,236
	11)	1469	12)	687		43)	40,880	44)	9792
	13)	567	14)	205		45)	30	46)	540
	15)	215	16)	141		47)	416	48)	2016
					IV	49)	2	50)	5
						51)	11	52)	0.05
II	17)	4	18)	2		53)	300	54)	9.41
	19)	6	20)	4		55)	2.196	56)	8.67
	21)	17	22)	13		57)	12.055	58)	105
	23)	17	24)	4		59)	12	60)	31
	25)	86	26)	31					
	27)	269	28)	524	V	61)	105	62)	8
	29)	2	30)	200		63)	118	64)	28
	31)	298	32)	9		65)	1		

SECTION III. ANSWER KEY   (from pages 32 through 40)

1.0

(1)		(a)	(b)	(c)	(d)
	1)	1 4/5	2 3/4	1 1/2	2 1/3
	2)	2	1 2/3	1 1/3	1
	3)	3 2/5	4 1/4	7	8 4/5
	4)	3 1/2	13 1/2	5 1/3	2 1/7
	5)	14 2/7	15 1/6	11 3/7	3 2/3
	6)	15	13 1/3	25	33 1/3
	7)	2 18/41	3 4/23	3 14/17	5 4/5

(2)	(a)	(b)	(c)	(d)	(e)
1)	4	4 3/4	8 5/6	14	17
2)	3 9/14	5 7/12	8 17/35	5 7/8	10 16/35
3)	7 7/12	17 1/12	8 11/12	11 5/6	22 5/12
4)	35 41/70	30 7/22	35 7/12	19 3/4	18 13/60
5)	20 2/9	11 19/20	10 1/70	71 5/6	16 39/40
6)	13 1/8				
7)	31 19/30				
8)	2 3/80				
9)	2 3/28				
10)	17 5/24				
11)	15 5/24				
12)	21 13/18				

2.0

(3) (a)

1)	9/2	4)	47/4	7)	82/9	10)	13/5
2)	15/4	5)	31/6	8)	23/7		
3)	57/8	6)	52/5	9)	10/9		

(b)

1)	8 1/2	4)	4 1/2	7)	3 2/7	10)	2 2/3
2)	5 1/5	5)	2 1/5	8)	1 1/4		
3)	4	6)	3 1/2	9)	5 7/19		

(4)	a)	2/3	3/4	3/4	4/5	8/9
	b)	7/10	1/2	8/9	5/6	1/8
	c)	3/4	3/5	1/4	2/5	9/16
	d)	2/5	2/3	1/3	1/3	2/5

(5)	a)	12/20	10/16	6/8	4/10
	b)	21/24	3/9	3/12	5/25
	c)	12/28	16/64	8/12	3/27

(6)	(a)	(b)	(c)	(d)	(e)
1)	5/4	5/3	5/6	4/5	4/5
2)	2/3	3/4	1	4/7	
3)	5/9	3/4	1/2	7/6	
4)	4/5	19/20	13/9	14/15	

(7)	(a)	(b)	(c)	(d)
1)	1 1/6	1 7/12	1 1/8	1/2
2)	3 11/12	7 3/4	2 7/9	5 1/14
3)	7 1/2	4 37/45	12 1/6	8 13/15
4)	9 7/30	10 2/3	9 7/60	7 1/3
5)	1 13/30			
6)	13 3/4			

(8)	(a)	(b)	(c)	(d)
1)	11/2	20/3	61/8	17/2
2)	43/4	71/6	180/7	123/20
3)	50/3	31/2	51/5	89/9
4)	152/3	121/3	41/4	61/5
5)	605/6	163/9	86/5	304/5
6)	31/11	10/3	64/9	65/9
7)	28/5	23/5	18/5	106/13
8)	37/6	63/10	96/13	82/15

(9)	(a)	(b)	(c)	(d)
1)	1/2	1/3	7/40	8/21
2)	1/9	1/18	3 1/6	2 1/12
3)	2 2/3	3/4	1 5/6	3 7/9
4)	19/20	7/8	5/6	13/36
5)	11/12			
6)	3 3/4			

(10)	(a)	(b)	(c)	(d)	(e)
1)	4 1/3	2 1/2	8 2/3	3 2/5	1 3/5
2)	3 1/4	3 1/2	7 8/21	1 1/18	14 3/28
3)	13 33/70	5/8	1 1/2	6 19/24	10 1/4
4)	3 17/20	23/30	1 3/14	3 2/5	6 3/7
5)	2 3/4				
6)	1 1/2				
7)	1 7/9				
8)	1/12				
9)	5 1/3				
10)	11/60				
11)	5 1/8; 15 − 9 7/8 = 5 1/8				
12)	9 7/20; 16 1/4 − 6 9/10 = 9 7/20				
13)	10 37/42; 14 5/7 − 3 5/6 = 10 37/42				
14)	4 5/9; 12 − 7 4/9 = 4 5/9				
15)	8 3/8; 16 3/8 − 8 = 8 3/8				

(11)

1) 3/8; 1/2 + 1/8 + ? = 1, 1/2 + 1/8 = 5/8, 1 − 5/8 = 3/8
2) 17/20; 5/8 = 25/40   17/20 = 34/40   34 is larger than 25
3) 4 7/9"; 10 2/3 − 5 8/9 = 4 7/9
4) 12′ 1 7/8"; 6′ 3 1/2" + 5′ 10 3/8" = 12′ 1 7/8"
   5 1/8"; 6′ 3 1/2" − 5′ 10 3/8" = 5 1/8"
5) 178′ 10 17/36"
6) 1/36 mile on second day
7) 5′ 7 7/24"
8) 1/6

(12)

	(a)	**(b)**	**(c)**	**(d)**
1)	5/9	1/12	1 1/4	1 11/24
2)	3/56	5/7	5 19/27	1/30
3)	10/63	1	7/10	5/16
4)	1/**6**	2 1/3	4 1/5	8/21

(13)

1) 5, 6 4/7, 9
2) 4, 40, 35
3) 1/5
4) $60
5) 1 2/9 hrs.
6) 3 1/5 years
7) 8 2/9 acres
8) Louise = 133 1/3 mi.; Laurie 1/3
   + Tommy   1/6 + Eddie   1/2 =
   400 miles Tommy = 66 2/3 mi.;
   1/3 × 400 = 133 1/3; 1/6 × 400
   = 66 2/3; 1/2 × 400 = 200 Eddie
   = 200 mi.

(14)

1)	5/16	**17)**	3 3/4
2)	1/6	**18)**	19 5/6
3)	5/27	**19)**	3 29/30
4)	1/6	**30)**	33 11/16
5)	1/20	**21)**	17 3/16
6)	3 3/4	**22)**	32
7)	9	**23)**	7 1/5
8)	4	**24)**	6 3/10
9)	1 7/20	**25)**	8
10)	1	**26)**	29 5/7
11)	1	**27)**	2 1/10
12)	1	**28)**	3 39/40
13)	3 5/7	**29)**	24
14)	2 8/21	**30)**	3 9/32
15)	17 3/5	**31)**	330 yd.
16)	22 2/5	**32)**	2 1/6 mi.

(15)

	(a)	**(b)**	**(c)**	**(d)**
1)	2	2 1/4	15	1 2/7
2)	27/28	3/5	2 7/24	1/2
3)	1 3/7	1 1/2	10/39	2 17/30
4)	1 7/15	2 1/12	3 7/10	9/10
5)	19 7/10			
6)	24 3/4			

7)	1 13/20
8)	5/28
9)	4/21
10)	16 ÷ 3/5
11)	16 1/2
12)	22 1/2

(16)

1. 3/4	**2.** 5	**3.** 1	**4.** 3
5. 1 1/5	**6.** 13 1/3	**7.** 5 1/7	**8.** 2/5
9. 3/5	**10.** 16/27	**11.** 9/25	**12.** 16/45
13. 5/14	**14.** 5 1/3	**15.** 7/60	**16.** 4/5
17. 3 59/75	**18.** 20/63	**19.** 21/32	**20.** 7/10
21. 7	**22.** 49/80	**23.** 1 5/16	**24.** 1 5/16
25. 9	**26.** 33 1/3	**27.** 9	**28.** 8/9
29. 20/21	**30.** 1 5/6	**31.** 1 17/48	**32.** 166 2/3″
33. 32/mi.	**34.** 16 1/3 gallons		

SECTION IV. ANSWER KEY (from pages 44 through 51)

1.0

(1)

	(a)	(b)	(c)	(d)
1.	4.82	5.21	29.3	343.73
2.	29.19	6.15	13.34	12.86

3.
 a. 15.06
 b. 60.33
 c. 2.964
 d. 120.57
 e. 68.09
 f. 150.78
 g. 173.16
 h. 136.53

4. 0.60
 3.2
 3.1

5.

	(a)	(b)	(c)	(d)
	3.07	5.01	7.67	8.51
	5.32	0.08	0.06	0.14

6. $1.41
7. $5.20

(2)

1. 0.5	**2.** 0.25	**3.** 0.3	**4.** 0.33
5. 0.71	**6.** 0.9	**7.** 0.8	**8.** 2.29
9. 3.13	**10.** 1.5	**11.** 0.6	**12.** 0.14

(3)

1. 1.43	**2.** 0.57	**3.** 5.35	**4.** 40.5
5. 10.75	**6.** 4.167	**7.** 10.52	**8.** 44.892
9. 0.333	**10.** 159.42	**11.** 6.949	**12.** 9.1
13. 3.67	**14.** 11.98	**15.** 9.1923	**16.** 33.13
17. 1.2	**18.** $12.55	**19.** 11.04	

(4)	(a)	(b)	(c)	(d)
1.	11.77	2.09	1.669	0.292
2.	87.9	11.11	38.48	155.17

3.
- a. 12.667
- b. 11.9
- c. 4.6
- d. 15.89
- e. 25.2
- f. 31.85
- g. 3.715
- h. 0.63

4. 30.8
5. 71.78
6. 143.65
7. $5315.32
8. $37.27
9. $3.94 billion
10. 2.37

(5)								
1.	2.6	2.	2.3	3.	0.6	4.	1.1
5.	6.5	6.	3.2	7.	3.6	8.	1.3
9.	4.5	10.	1.16	11.	2.7	12.	576.64
13.	25.55	14.	4.36	15.	33.4	16.	29.4
17.	12.86	18.	3.29	19.	0.8	20.	11.2
21.	35.25	22.	2.48	23.	18.5	24.	$7.12
25.	2.9 seconds						

(6)		(a)	(b)	(c)	(d)
	1.	1.86	0.074	34.953	1.324
	2.	5.148	0.0012	18.336	435.6
	3.	563	56.3	563	0.0563
	4.	662	7.403	0.0073	0.0832
	5.	0.147	2.565	15.21	413.93

6. $3.48; $0.29 each, $0.29 × 12 = $3.48
7. $4.29; 42.9¢ per gallon, 42.9¢ × 10 = 429¢ = $4.29
8. 414.12 miles; 19.72 miles/gallon, 19.72 × 21 = 414.12
9. $2982.20; $57.35/week, 52 weeks = 1 year, $57.35 × 52 = $2982.20
10. 27.075 minutes; 4.75 × 5.7 = 27.075

(7)										
1)	5.68	2)	0.12	3)	1.5	4)	3.2	5)	6.1
6)	4.004	7)	18.88	8)	24.92	9)	0.352	10)	70.06
11)	0.27	12)	695.2	13)	3.339	14)	70.11	15)	480.32
16)	34.375	17)	2676.3	18)	0.624	19)	780.7	20)	0.823

21) 23.4; 0.72 of 32.5 = ? 0.72 × 32.5 = 23.4
22) 16.2
23) 61.2
24) 114.18; product of 17.3 and 6.6?, 17.3 × 6.6 = 114.18
25) 33.6; 3.2 is ? times as great as 10.5, 3.2 × 10.5 = 33.6
26) $200; 3.2 × $62.50 = $200
27) 144.75

(8)

1) 220	**2)** 64.3	**3)** 4
4) 0.3	**5)** 702	**6)** 20
7) 33.4	**8)** 70	**9)** 2474.7
10) 59	**11)** 30.2	**12)** 7645.1
13) 0.4	**14)** 0.4	**15)** 26.1
16) 9.1	**17)** 125	**18)** 4
19) 67	**20)** 6.3	**21)** 101
22) 1000	**23)** 3	**24)** 30,000
25) 0.01	**26)** 133.3	**27)** 200
28) 0.6, (0.5714285)	**29)** 6.5	

(9)

I
1) 50%	**2)** 25%	**3)** 33%	**4)** 66%	**5)** 70%
6) 20%	**7)** 30%	**8)** 70%	**9)** 80%	**10)** 90%
11) 12.5%	**12)** 6.5%	**13)** 8%	**14)** 9%	**15)** 1.1%
16) 123%	**17)** 350%	**18)** 500%	**19)** 100%	**20)** 400%

II
21) 26; 20% of 130, 0.2 × 130 = 26
22) 30
23) 6
24) 240
25) 21.25
26) 35.28
27) 45; 300% of 15, 3.00 × 15 = 45
28) 63.84

	(a)	(b)	(c)	(d)	(e)
(10)	3.6	0.8	1.3	7.6	8.1
(11)	3.62	5.89	6.03	4.11	0.01
(12)	0.058	0.774	0.395	8.808	5.063

(13)
	(a)	(b)	(c)	(d)
1.	601	50.3	75	20
2.	6	600	3.5	90
3.	4	20	60	8.48
4.	0.08	300	0.55	0.02

5. 31.5; 15.75 ÷ 0.5 = 31.5
6. 70; 49 ÷ 0.7 = 70
7. 30; 12 ÷ 0.4 = 30
8. 232; 116 ÷ 0.5 = 232
9. 17.78; 16 ÷ 0.9 = 17.7777 = 17.78

(14)	(a)	(b)	(c)	(d)
1.	0.5	0.75	0.6	0.4
2.	1.5	1.25	0.8	1.0

(15)	(a)	(b)	(c)	(d)
1.	0.38	0.83	0.88	0.56
2.	1.60	0.57	0.82	0.67

		(a)	(b)	(c)
(1)	1.	250	440	760
	2.	75	45.83	777.78
	3.	833.33	100	375
	4.	211.27	149.25	10,000
	5.	4.5	500	625

6. 541.67; 12% of whole = 65, whole $= \dfrac{65}{12\%} = \dfrac{65}{0.12} = 541.67$

7. 17.5

8. 375

9. 832.73

10. 200; 20% of games won; total games won $= \dfrac{40}{20\%} = 200$

11. 20 total; 90% of total = 18, total $= \dfrac{18}{90\%} = \dfrac{18}{0.9} = 20$ total

   2 wrong $20 - 18 = 2$ wrong

12. $109

13. 3000

14. $150,000

15. $32.14; 42% of bill = $13.50, total $= \dfrac{\$13.50}{42\%} = \dfrac{\$13.50}{0.42} = 32.14$

16. 300

17. 6.7 feet

18. 161.6 tons

19. $22.43

20. 30 hours

SECTION V. ANSWER KEY (from page 55)

(1)		(a)	(b)	(c)	(d)
	1.	4/25	4/5	7/40	9/20
	2.	7/20	1/25	17/100	3/500
	3.	18/25	14/25	11/25	9/250
	4.	a. 3/4	b. 0.88	c. 1/12	
		d. 5/8	e. 2/3	f. 8/9	

5.

	Won
Boston	72/115; 0.63
New York	13/22; 0.59
Atlanta	61/115; 0.53
Baltimore	45/115; 0.39
Kansas City	20/115; 0.17

SECTION VI. ANSWER KEY (from page 59)

(1)										
	1.	a. 50%	b. 80%	c. 70%	d. 43%	e. 63%
	2.	f. 75%	g. 217%	h. 250%	i. 333%	j. 45%
	3.	k. 38%	l. 39%	m. 31%	n. 533%	o. 525%

4. 47% won, 53% lost; 47/100 = 0.47 × 100% = 47%
5. 86% correct, 14% wrong; 50 − 7 = 43, 43/50 = 0.86 × 100% = 86%
6. 62 1/2% cream, 37 1/2% flour; 3 + 5 = 8, 5/8 = 0.625 × 100% = 62 1/2%
7. 37%; 37/100 = 0.37 × 100% = 37%
8. 17/20 correct; 3/20 incorrect; 85% = 85/100 = 17/20
9. 23/50; 46% = 0.46 = 46/100 = 23/50
10. 11/25 morning, 51/100 afternoon, 1/20 evening
11. 11/50; 22% = 22/100 = 11/50
12. 7/8, 0.875, 87 1/2%; 42/48 = 7/8, 7/8 = 0.875, 0.875 × 100% = 87 1/2

(from page 60)

(1)		(a)	(b)	(c)
	1.	105	13.6	185.56
	2.	46.8	262.5	76.16
	3.	3.2	16.28	32.5
	4.	21	36.9	91.2
	5.	30.6	15.75	87.375
	6.	$150	$2.75	$59.85
	7.	$15	$2.59	$63.21

8. 1105; 85% of 1300 = 0.85 × 1300 = 1105
9. $63; 45% of $140 = 0.45 × 140 = 63
10. 7.8 oz.; 65% of 12 = 0.65 × 12 = 7.8
11. 2 days
12. 4,960,000

13. 42 hours or 15% of work hours; 15% of 280 = 42, $\frac{42}{280} = 0.15 = 15\%$

14. 135 girls, 405 boys

15. 9960

16. 386 for, 419 against

17. $2137.50 books   25% of $8550 = $\frac{25}{100}$ × 8550 = 2137.50

$4104.00 reading equipment   48% of $8550 = $\frac{48}{100}$ × 8550 = 4104.00

$2308.50 transportation   27% of $8550 = $\frac{27}{100}$ × 8550 = 2308.50

18. $84,000

63

(from page 61)

		(a)	**(b)**	**(c)**
(1)	**1.**	53%	50%	12.5%
	2.	20%	66 2/3%	200%
	3.	20%	91.3%	80%
	4.	2555%	74%	82%
	5.	5%		
	6.	0.75%		
	7.	44.3%		
	8.	197%		
	9.	96%		
	10.	62.5%		
	11.	61%		
	12.	20%		
	13.	59% won, 41% lost		
	14.	9.6%		
	15.	12.5% (8 pints = 1 gal.)		
	16.	7.5% (2000 lb. = 1 ton)		
	17.	25% (32 liquid oz. = 1 qt.)		
	18.	77.8% right, 22.2% wrong		
	19.	16.7%		
	20.	77%		
	21.	25%		
	22.	78.9%		
	23.	50%, 66 2/3%		
	24.	43% (0.70 − 0.49 = 0.21)		

25. 5.6% $(36 - 34 = 2, \frac{2}{36} = 5.6)$

26. 23%   **28.** 50%

27. 33%   **29.** 17%

30. 20%

31. 10%

32. 167%

33. 200%

34. 76%

35. 350%

36. 160

37. 200

38. 25

39. 25

40. 20

41. 10

42. 250

SECTION VII. ANSWER KEY (from pages 68 through 72)

(1)

	(a)	(b)	(c)	(d)
1.	16	52	54	34
2.	25	26.5	8.5	47
3.	46	67.6	42.8	60.0

(2)

	(a)	(b)	(c)
1.	96	1100	336
2.	326.25	63.33	1560.6
3.	2448.24	181.3	1005

(3)

	(a)	(b)	(c)
1.	20′	30′	8″
2.	15.5′	17.44′	21.82
3.	9.2′	23.5′	51.2′

(4)
1. 69′; 19 1/2′ by 15′, $P = 2l + 2w$, $P = 2 \times 19\ 1/2 + 2 \times 15 = 69′$
2. 206.62 ft.^{2}; $A = l \times w$, $A = 15\ 1/2 \times 13\ 1/3 = 206.66$ ft.^{2}
3. 6500 sq. yds.; $A = l \times w$, $A = 100 \times 65 = 6500$
4. 16″; $A = l \times w$, $332 = l \times 20\ 3/4$, $l = \dfrac{332}{20\ 3/4} = 16″$
5. 1300.5 sq. ft.

(5)

a) 20   b) 26   c) 23.2   d) 42   e) 121.2
f) 4   g) 68.8

(6)

a) 272.25 sq. in.   b) 33.64 sq. ft.   c) 3612.01 sq. yds.   d) 39.063 sq. ft.
e) 28.44 sq. ft.   f) 434.03 sq. in.   g) 492.84 sq. ft.   h) 43.56 sq. in.
i) 237.16 sq. in.   j) 424.36 sq. ft.

(7)
1. 8100 sq. ft.
2. 60 yds.
3. 241.6 ft.
4. $675
5. 400 sq. in.
6. 625 sq. ft.

(8)

	(a)	(b)	(c)	(d)
1.	17.5	25	160	12
2.	82.5	25.83	102	28.5
3.	155.8	52.29	70.56	0.45

(9)

1.	308	**5.**	62.86	**9.**	198
2.	176	**6.**	25.14	**10.**	56.57
3.	440	**7.**	47.14		
4.	44	**8.**	125.71		

(10)
1. 452.16
2. 50.24
3. 31,400
4. 78.5
5. 706.5
6. 1962.5
7. 128.61
8. 243.16
9. 116.84
10. 84.91

(11)
1. 25
2. 35
3. 10
4. 20
5. 15

(12)
1. 5
2. 5
3. 13
4. 1
5. 0.5

Questions (from pages 73 and 74)

(13)
1. True
2. True
3. True
4. c
5. b

(14)
1. a
2. c
3. 1) A_S; 2) P_R; 3) P_S; 4) A_R
4. principal; rate; time
5. product; time
6. distance; time
7. one half; base; altitude
8. product; pi (π); radius
9. product; pi; radius
10. volume; product; length; height; depth

Questions (from pages 75)

(15)
1. True
2. True
3. True

Exercises (from pages 75 and 76)

(16)
1. $12 / x = 3$
2. $12 / x = 3y$
3. $(12 - 3) = 3x$
4. $x / 2y = 5$
5. $(16 - x) / 2 = 6$
6. $x - 9 = 5x$
7. $5 + 3 = 2x$
8. $x / 5 + 3 = 2y$

(17)
1. $x = 3 \cdot 10$
2. $x = 20 - 3$ ($3)
3. $x = 16 - 7$
4. $x + 2x = 21$
5. $x / 2 = \$25.00$

(18)
1. f
2. b
3. d
4. c
5. f
6. h
7. a
8. e
9. g
10. e

SECTION VII. ANSWER KEY (from pages 79 and 80)

(1) a. 216   b. 49   c. 256   d. 15625   e. 2401   f. 32   g. 81

(2) a. 7^2 d. 1^4 g. 20^2
     b. 6^4 e. 10^3 h. 50^4
     c. 5^3 f. 2^6 i. 9^6

(3) a. 49   d. 1000   g. 343   j. 10000
     b. 216   e. 10   h. 400   k. 525
     c. 32   f. 1   i. 1600   l. 256
     m. 6^2
     n. 2^3
     o. 10^4
     p. 5^3
     q. 4^3
     r. 2^6

(4) 1. 5000   7. 147.6
     2. 3150   8. 164.8
     3. 7   9. 687.5
     4. 512   10. 82
     5. 270   11. 5120
     6. 350   12. 200

(5) a. $(a + b)$ h. $(5 - a)$
     b. $(c - d)$ i. k^5
     c. $2h$ j. $(a + b + d)$
     d. $a \cdot b \cdot c$ k. $(c - b)$
     e. $a/3$ l. b/a
     f. $\dfrac{a \cdot b}{3}$ m. $2(x + y)$
     g. $(h + 5)$ n. $\dfrac{(b + h)}{2}$

SECTION IX. ANSWER KEY (from pages 83 through 92)

(1)
1. $(n + 3)$
2. $3X$
3. $(y - 3); (y + 5)$
4. $X/3$
5. $12Z; K/12$
6. $2C$
7. $(d + 4)$
8. $(a + b)$
9. $(d - 6)$
10. $4X$
11. $a/2$
12. nickels $= 3X$; quarters $= X/4$

(2)
1. $12x$
2. $9a$
3. $5/6y$
4. $5.5a$
5. $2y$
6. $2.18b$
7. c
8. $2.2z$
9. $4a + 8h$
10. $21x + 7y$
11. $14x + 3y$
12. $4d - 4y$
13. e
14. $8y$
15. $7a + 3x + 3y$
16. $2a + b + 3h$

(3)
1. 40
2. 24
3. 10
4. 28
5. 10
6. 2000
7. 49
8. 4
9. 14.7
10. 15

(4)

	(a)	(b)	(c)	(d)	(e)
1.	-12	$+8$	-14	$+11$	-3
2.	$+8$	0	$+9$	-14	$+4$
3.	-129	-460	-7	-363	-1

(5)

	(a)	(b)	(c)	(d)	(e)
1.	-1	$+3$	$+241$	$+46$	$+153$
2.	-100	$+21.5$	$+201.73$	$+41.3$	0
3.	$+8\,1/4$	$+7\,1/4$	-10	$+15\,1/3$	$+7\,5/8$

(6)

	(a)	(b)	(c)	(d)	(e)
1.	$+48$	-45	$+300$	-1050	$+120$
2.	-24	$-14\,5/8$	$+200$	$+40$	$+38$
3.	$+8\,1/3$	$-24\,3/5$	$+80$	-20	$+450$
4.	-360				
5.	$+256.2$				
6.	$-1/24$				
7.	-131				
8.	-210				
9.	-72				
10.	-125				

(7)

	(a)	(b)	(c)	(d)	(e)
1.	−4	+4	10	−4	−4 2/5
2.	+11	−10 1/3	−2 4/5	−6 2/3	−11
3.	−0.67	−7.11	−0.05	+20	−12

(8)

1.	9	2.	36	3.	3	4.	12	5.	36
6.	6	7.	8	8.	16	9.	22	10.	9
11.	8	12.	1	13.	4	14.	3 1/2	15.	−13
16.	−20	17.	100	18.	64	19.	32	20.	17

(9)

1.	$x = 4$	$x = 5$	$x = 5$	$x = 30$
2.	$x = 9$	$x = 1$	$x = 12$	$x = 54$

(10)

	(a)	(b)	(c)	(d)
1.	$x = 21$	$x = 40$	$x = 10$	$x = 19$
2.	$x = 13$	$x = 7$	$x = 13$	$x = 15$
3.	$x = 20$	$x = 30$	$x = -80$	$x = -35$

(11)

	(a)	(b)	(c)	(d)
1.	$x = 10$	$x = 4$	$x = 7$	$x = 11$
2.	$x = 10$	$x = 20$	$x = 4$	$x = -5$
3.	$x = -10$	$x = -1/4$	$x = -3$	$x = -6$

(12)

	(a)	(b)	(c)	(d)
1.	$x = 15$	$x = 24$	$x = -35$	$x = 120$
2.	$x = 10$	$x = 360$	$x = 4$	$x = 72$
3.	$x = -100$	$x = -25$	$x = 90$	$x = -88$

(13)

	(a)	(b)	(c)	(d)
1.	$x = 5$	$x = 1$	$x = 2$	$x = 2$
2.	$x = 7\ 2/3$	$x = 80$	$x = 216$	$x = 6$
3.	$x = 24$	$x = 17$	$x = 24$	$x = 15$
4.	$x = 1/5$	$x = 25$	$x = 13\ 1/2$	$x = 32$
5.	$x = 9$	$x = 100$	$x = 1.2$	$x = 2$
6.	4
7.	18
8.	15
9.	$46
10.	22
11.	1 1/2
12.	25
13.	8 1/2
14.	14
15.	45
16.	25

SECTION X. ANSWER KEY (from pages 95 and 96)

(1) **1.** 300; R × T = D, 60 × 5 = 300
2. 216
3. 246.05

4. 195; R × T = D, 60 × 3 1/4 = $\frac{60}{1} \times \frac{13}{4} = 195$

(15 min. = 1/4 hour)

5. 116 2/3; R × T = D, 50 × 2 1/3 = $\frac{50}{1} \times \frac{7}{3} = 116\ 2/3$

(20 min. = 1/3 hour)
6. 175

7. 720 miles; R × T = D, 90 × 8 = 720
(1 1/2 hours = 90 minutes)

8. 4 1/6; R × T = D, 5 × 5/6 = $\frac{5}{1} \times \frac{5}{6} = 4\ 1/6$

(50 min. = 5/6 hour)
9. 35
10. 7 1/3 mi.

(2) **1.** 100; D ÷ T = R, 600 ÷ 6 = $\frac{600}{6} = 100$

2. 16
3. 75 mph
4. 80 mph
5. 187.5 mph

(3) **1.** 5; T = D ÷ R, 350 ÷ 70 = $\frac{350}{70} = 5$

2. 4.5
3. 3/4

4. 8:12 PM; T = D ÷ R, 480 ÷ 150 = $\frac{480}{150} = 3\ 1/5$,

1/5 of 60 min. = 12 min., total time is 3 hours 12 min.
leave 5:00 PM plus 3 hrs. and 12 min. = 8:12 PM

5. 5 1/2 hrs; T = D ÷ R, $\frac{2200}{400} = 5\ 1/2$ hours

SECTION XI. ANSWER KEY   (from page 100)

(1) 1. $20; I = P × R × T, $400 × 5\% × 1 = 400 × \dfrac{5}{100} × 1 = 20$

   2. $70
   3. $250

   4. $450; I = P × R × T, $3000 × 5\% × 3 = 3000 × \dfrac{5}{100} × 3 = 450$

   5. $30
   6. $20
   7. $1200
   8. $90
   9. $84

   10. $61; I = P × R × T, $4000 × 6.1\% × 1/4 = 4000 × \dfrac{6.1}{100} × \dfrac{1}{4} = 61$

       (3 mos. = 1/4 year)

(2)

   1. 7%; R = I ÷ PT, $R = \dfrac{350}{5000 × 1} = 0.07$, $0.07 × 100 = 7\%$

   2. $27; I = P × R × T, $I = 900 × \dfrac{6}{100} × \dfrac{1}{2} = 27$

       (6 mos. = 1/2 year)

   3. 2 yrs. 4 mo.; $T = \dfrac{I}{P × R}$, $T = \dfrac{490}{3000 × 0.07} = 2\ 1/3 = 2$ yrs. 4 mo.

       (7% = 0.07)

   4. 600; $P = \dfrac{I}{R × T}$, $P = \dfrac{24}{0.08 × 1/2} = 600$

   5. $510; I = P × R × T, $I = 2000 × 8\% × 1 = 160$
       $I = 3500 × 10\% × 1 = 350$
       Total interest = 160 + 350 = $510

   6. 1 1/2%; 6% per year interest in 1/4 year = 1/4 of 6% = 1 1/2%

   7. $20,000; $P = \dfrac{I}{R × T}$, $P = \dfrac{500}{0.05 × 1/2} = 20{,}000$

   8. $600 at 6%; I = P × R × T, $I = 500 × 7\% × 1 = \$350$
       $I = 600 × 6\% × 1 = \$360$

   9. $2270; I = 2000 × 6\% × 2\ 1/4 = 270
       Total amount = 2000 + 270 = 2270

10. 2.73 yrs.; Interest is $300 on $2000 principal

$$\text{Time} = \frac{I}{P \times R} = \frac{300}{2000 \times 0.055}$$

$$\text{Time} = 2.73$$

SECTION XII. ANSWER KEY (from page 103 and 105)

(1)
1. 1260
2. 8000
3. 30
4. 160
5. 28.6
6. 12 3/16
7. 154
8. 613.272
9. 10 1/2
10. 36,000

(2)
1. 4"; $V = I \times w \times d$, $d = \dfrac{V}{I \times w}$, $d = \dfrac{240}{10 \times 6} = 4$

2. 20 ft.; $V = I \times w \times d$, $I = w = d$
$V = 1 \times 1 \times 1$, $V = 1^3$, $^3\sqrt{V} = 1$, $^3\sqrt{1000} = 1$
$1 = 10$, $21 = 20$

3. 192 cubic feet

4. No; $V = I \times w \times d$, $V = \dfrac{3}{4} \times 1\dfrac{1}{4} \times \dfrac{1}{2} = \dfrac{3}{4} \times \dfrac{5}{4} \times \dfrac{1}{2} = 15/32$

   15/32 cubic feet, 1 cubic foot = 1728 cubic inches needed to fill tank

5. 10800 cubic feet; $V = I \times w \times d = 25 \times 10 \times 2 = 500$ cubic yards $\times$ 27 cubic feet
   = 1350 cubic feet
   80% of 13500 = 10800 cubic feet
   (NOTE: 27 cubic feet = 1 cubic yard)

(3)
1. 50.29 sq. feet; $A = \pi R^2 = \dfrac{22}{7} \times R^2 = \dfrac{22}{7} \times 4 \times 4 = 50.29$

2. YES; $A = \dfrac{22}{7} \times R^2$ Area $= \dfrac{22}{7} \times 64 = 201.06$ sq. feet

   $201.06 \times 2 = 402.12$ sq. feet
   $30 \times 20 = 600$ sq. feet available; ans. YES

3.   Small circle area = 154 sq. inches $\pi R^2 = A$ $R = 7$, $A_1 = \dfrac{22}{7} \times 7$

Area shaded portion = 226 sq. inches

Larger circle: $A_1 = \dfrac{22}{7} \times 49$

$$\text{Area}_2 = \dfrac{22}{7} \times (7 + 4)^2 \qquad A_1 = 154$$

$$= \dfrac{22}{7} \times (11)^2$$

$$A_2 = 380$$

$$\begin{array}{r} 380 \\ -154 \\ \hline 226 \text{ sq. inches} \end{array}$$

4.   Area field = $l \times w = 50 \times 30 = 1500$ sq. yds.

Area circle = $\pi R^2 = \dfrac{22}{7} \times 6^2 = \dfrac{22}{7} \times 36 = 113.14$

$$\begin{array}{ll} \text{Diameter} = 12 \text{ yds.} & \qquad 1500.00 \\ \text{Radius} \quad = 6 \text{ yds.} & \qquad -113.14 \\ & \qquad \overline{1386.86} \end{array}$$

Ans. = 1386.96 sq. yds.

5. $R = 6''$ $A = \pi R^2$ $= 3.14$ $A = 113.04$ sq. inches
$A = 452.16$ sq. inches $113.04 = 3.14$ R^2
$R^2 = 113.04/3.14 = 36$
$R^2 = 36$
$R = \sqrt{36} = 6$
$2R = 12$, $A = ?$ $A = \pi R^2$
$A = 3.14 \times (12)^2 = 3.14 \times 144$
$A = 452.16$ sq. inches

SECTION XIII. ANSWER KEY (from pages 109 and 110)

(1)   **1.** $100 $300 \times 1/3 = 100$

2. $15

3. $191.25 $225 \times 15\% = 225 \times 0.15 = 33.75$

$$\begin{array}{r} 225.00 \\ -33.75 \\ \hline 191.25 \end{array}$$

4. $378 $500 \times 16\% = 80$; $500 - 80 = 420$ $\begin{array}{r} 80 \\ +42 \\ \hline 122 \end{array}$
$420 \times 10\% = 42$

$$500 - 122 = 378$$

5. 12 1/2%   % discount × selling price = amount of discount

$$\% \text{ discount} = \frac{\text{amount of discount}}{\text{selling price}}$$

$$\begin{array}{r} 320 \\ -280 \\ \hline 40 \end{array}$$

$$\% = \frac{40}{320} = \frac{1}{8} = .125$$

$$.125 \times 100\% = 12.5\%$$

6. $560

7. $3500   1000 × 250% = 2500   1000 + 2500 = 3500

8. $2240   1600 × 15% = 240; 1840 × 25% = 400

$$\begin{array}{r} 1600 \\ +240 \\ \hline 1840 \end{array} \qquad \begin{array}{r} 1840 \\ +400 \\ \hline 2240 \end{array}$$

9. $112.50   75 × (25%) = 18.75; 93.75 × 20% = 18.75

$$\begin{array}{r} 75.00 \\ +18.75 \\ \hline 93.75 \end{array} \qquad \begin{array}{r} 93.75 \\ +18.75 \\ \hline 112.50 \end{array}$$

10. $277.78 $\% \text{ discount} = \dfrac{\text{amount discount}}{\text{selling price}}$; $18\% = \dfrac{50}{\text{selling price}}$

$$\text{selling price} = \frac{50}{18\%}$$

$$\text{selling price} = \$277.78$$

SECTION XIV. ANSWER KEY (from pages 113 and 114)

(1)

	(a)	(b)	(c)
1.	2/1	10/1	7/2
2.	5/6	2/3	5/1
3.	2/1	b/a	x/y
4.	1/1	4/1	3/1

(2) **1.** $100 $\dfrac{6}{5} = \dfrac{120}{?},$ $5 \times 120 = 6 \times ?,$ $\dfrac{600}{6} = ?, ? = 100$

2. 28 hours $\dfrac{\text{Brown}}{\text{Swanson}} = \dfrac{4}{7};$ $\dfrac{4}{7} = \dfrac{\text{Brown}}{49};$ $\dfrac{4 \times 49}{7} = \text{Brown} = 28$

3. 32 miles   Ratio of A to B is $\dfrac{8}{3}$, $\dfrac{8}{3} = \dfrac{A}{12};$ $\dfrac{8 \times 12}{3} = A = 32$

(3) **1.** 20 girls $\dfrac{4}{3} = \dfrac{?}{15};$ $\dfrac{4 \times 15}{3} = ? = 20$

2. 1 cup

3. 60 years

4. $35,000

5. 5 miles $\quad \dfrac{\text{Franklin}}{\text{Boston}} = \dfrac{2/5}{2/3}; \quad \dfrac{2/5}{2/3} = \dfrac{3}{x}$ miles, x = 5 miles

6. $24,000 $\quad \dfrac{6}{5}$ ratio; 6x + 5x = 44,000 $\quad$ ①

and $\hspace{5.5cm}$ 11x = 44,000 $\quad$ ②

$20,000 $\hspace{4cm}$ x = $\dfrac{44,000}{11}$ $\quad$ ③

$\hspace{5cm}$ x = 4,000 $\quad$ ④
$\hspace{4.4cm}$ 6x = 24,000 $\quad$ ⑤
$\hspace{4.4cm}$ 5x = 20,000 $\quad$ ⑥

7. 7 1/2, 15, 37 1/2 $\quad$ 5:2:1 proportion;

$$5x + 2x + 1x = 60$$
$$8x = 60$$

$$x = \frac{60}{8}$$

$$x = 7\ 1/2$$
$$5x = 37\ 1/2$$
$$2x = 15$$

SECTION XV. ANSWER KEY (from pages 118 through 121)

(1) **1.** Between $10,000 and $20,000
$\hspace{0.9cm}$ **2.** Less than $3000
$\hspace{0.9cm}$ **3.** Affluent
$\hspace{0.9cm}$ **4.** B

(2) **1.** Yes
$\hspace{0.9cm}$ **2.** No
$\hspace{0.9cm}$ **3.** 2:1 $\quad$ 16%/8% = 2:1
$\hspace{0.9cm}$ **4.** Tobacco and grain
$\hspace{0.9cm}$ **5.** Citrus

(3) **Unemployment in %**
$\hspace{0.9cm}$ varied; 1930, 1940, 1970; 1950; greater unemployment

(4) **Graph of Biology Test Results**
$\hspace{0.9cm}$ 2; majority of class scored in same range

(5) **Area**
$\hspace{0.9cm}$ 200,000 sq. mi.; 2:1

(6)   **Comparison of Male and Female Grade**
foreign language; English; History and Natural Science;
Area according to best level of achievement

SIMULATED G.E.D. MATHEMATICS EXAMINATION ANSWER KEY (from page 125)

1.	d	26.	e
2.	c	27.	a
3.	a	28.	c
4.	a	29.	b
5.	c	30.	b
6.	a	31.	c
7.	d	32.	c
8.	a	33.	d
9.	c	34.	a
10.	b	35.	e
11.	e	36.	d
12.	b	37.	a
13.	e	38.	b
14.	e	39.	c
15.	a	40.	b
16.	d	41.	b
17.	b	42.	d
18.	c	43.	b
19.	b	44.	b
20.	c	45.	a
21.	d	46.	b
22.	c	47.	c
23.	b	48.	b
24.	a	49.	c
25.	e	50.	b